A.D. Ramsli
Edmonton, Alta, Canada.
484-7651

$2-95

AUSTRALIAN MARSUPIALS

AUSTRALIAN MARSUPIALS

KEITH DAVEY

PERIWINKLE BOOKS

First published 1970 by Lansdowne Press, Melbourne
This hardback edition with corrections published 1976
by Periwinkle Books, an imprint of
Books for Pleasure Pty Limited
176 South Creek Road, Dee Why West NSW Australia 2099

Typeset by Dudley E. King, Melbourne
Printed and bound in Hong Kong

ISBN 0 7018 0641 9

Cover photograph by Michael Morcombe

Frontispiece: Head of Grey Kangaroo

Acknowledgement

The photographs of the Dibbler (p. 17), Honey Possum (p. 36), Pigmy Possum (p. 45), Squirrel Glider (p. 45), Sugar Glider (p. 46), Green Ringtail Possum (p. 47), Western Ringtail Possum (p. 46), and Koala (p. 57) are by Michael Morcombe. The photograph of the Wombat (p. 48) is by J. Byrne.
The sequence on page 13 is by Ederic Slater (CSIRO) from the book *Kangaroos* by H. J. Frith and J. A. Calaby.

CONTENTS

Introduction

WHAT IS A MARSUPIAL?

Marsupial is the scientific name given to a group of mammals in which the females possess a pouch (called in Latin the *marsupium*) in which the young develop after they are born prematurely. A more detailed description of marsupial birth is given later. Kangaroos and wallabies are probably the best-known examples of Australian marsupials, which also include possums, wombats, and the koala.

Marsupials are now found in only two parts of the world, North and South America and Australia. About 120 species are found on the Australian mainland and Tasmania.

Evolution The Australian marsupials have descended from ancestors which developed in America. They probably came into existence about 120 million years ago. Somehow the forebears of today's species found their way to the Australian continent: perhaps across land bridges which once joined the continents, or perhaps on floating rafts of vegetation and other debris. These ancestral forms have, over the ages, adapted to Australian conditions, and are now quite varied in form, ranging from the little Marsupial Mice to the Red Kangaroo. Some burrow, some hop, some climb trees and some can glide through the air.

Scientific Classification Scientists divide all living things into groups which share common characteristics. The three primary groups are animals, plants and protists (simple organisms such as algae, bacteria, fungi, etc.). Animals comprise about thirty main groups, each of which is called a PHYLUM (plural phyla). The phyla are divided into CLASSES which in turn are divided into ORDERS. The orders are further divided into FAMILIES which consist of a number of GENERA (Singular: genus). Finally, each genus consists of a number of SPECIES.

This account is necessarily very simplified. In fact, there are other divisions within the system, such as sub-class, sub-order and sub-species.

Squirrel Glider (p. 60)

Scientific names Every species recognised by science is given a scientific name. The same name is used by scientists in all countries—unlike the common name, which may vary from one place to another—and is always written in Latin. The name of the genus is written first, followed by the specific name. Thus *Sminthopsis murina* is the species *murina* of the Genus *Sminthopsis*. The scientific name is written in italics and the generic name is given a capital letter. In technical literature the name of the person who first described the species is often written after the specific name in ordinary type.

This system of classification is known as the binominal system. If the scientific name contains three words a sub-species is denoted. For instance *Isoodon macrourus torosus* is a sub-species of the Brindled Bandicoot, *Isoodon macrourus*.

Classification of Marsupials The phylum Chordata is divided into a number of sub-phyla. One of these is the sub-phylum Vertebrata (vertebrates). This contains many classes, one of which is the class Mammalia (mammals i.e. warm-blooded animals which suckle their young). The mammals are divided into two sub-classes—Prototheria (including monotremes or egg-laying mammals) and Theria. The Theria contains the Metatheria (Marsupials) and Eutheria (Placental Mammals).

Early authorities placed all the world's marsupials in a single order, the Marsupialia, but modern zoologists recognize a number of different marsupial orders. But, as there is no general agreement yet on the exact limits of these orders, the Australian marsupials are treated in this book in two main groups—the Polyprotodont Marsupials (with 6 incisor teeth in the lower jaw), and the Diprotodont Marsupials (with the functional lower incisors reduced to a pair of large forward-pointing teeth).

The families of Australian marsupials are also under review at present, and some scientists believe that there should be at least three separate families for our possums. On the other hand, the number of recognized genera is being reduced. Some species groups have recently been advised, and there is a tendency too to disregard the great number of sub-species names that have been given in the

Top: A Narrow-footed Marsupial Mouse (p. 27)
Below: Northern Native Cat (p. 32)

GROUPING OF THE AUSTRALIAN MARSUPIAL FAMILIES AND THE RELATIONSHIP OF MARSUPIALS TO OTHER MAMMALS

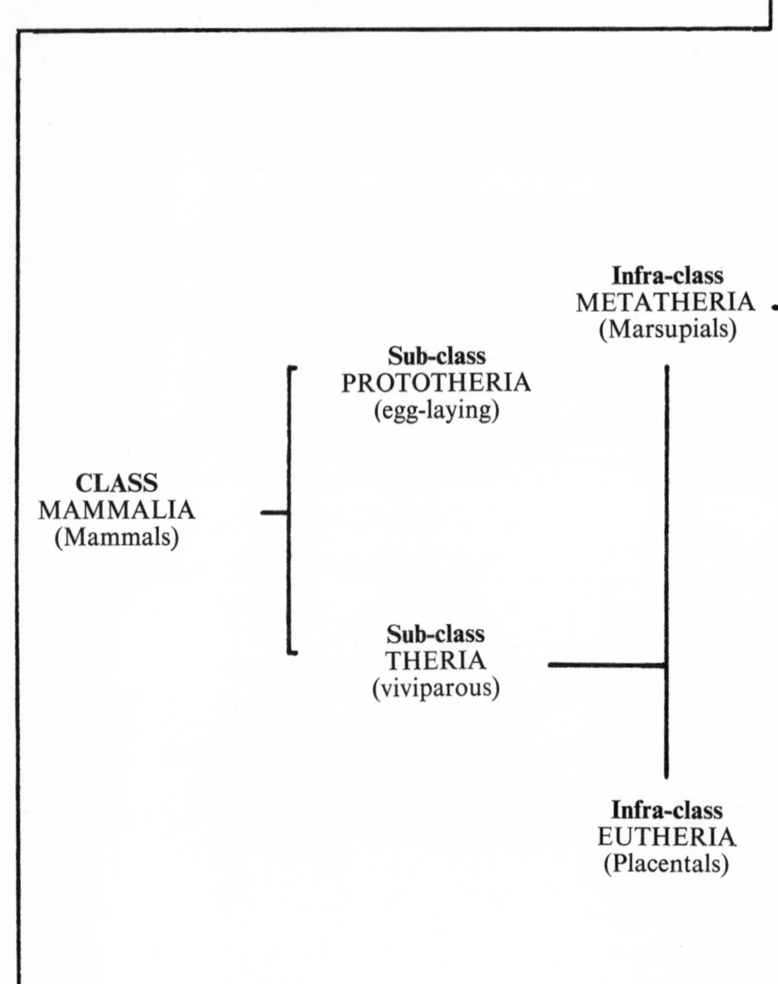

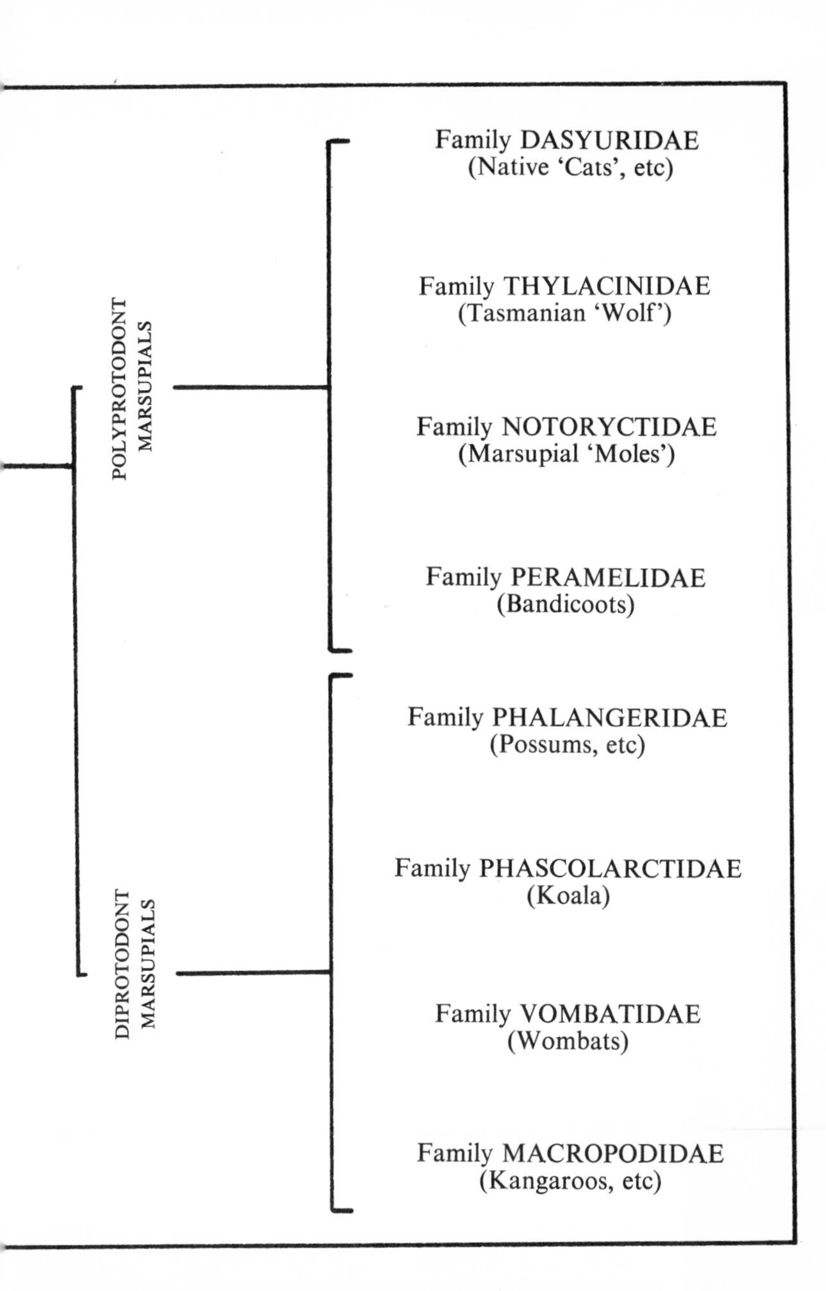
POLYPROTODONT MARSUPIALS
DIPROTODONT MARSUPIALS
Family DASYURIDAE
(Native 'Cats', etc)
Family THYLACINIDAE
(Tasmanian 'Wolf')
Family NOTORYCTIDAE
(Marsupial 'Moles')
Family PERAMELIDAE
(Bandicoots)
Family PHALANGERIDAE
(Possums, etc)
Family PHASCOLARCTIDAE
(Koala)
Family VOMBATIDAE
(Wombats)
Family MACROPODIDAE
(Kangaroos, etc)

past to more-or-less minor variants of many species. Therefore, very few races or sub-species are noted in this book.

Marsupial birth The three groups of mammals each give birth to their young in a different fashion. Monotremes, which include the Platypus and the Spiny Anteater, lay eggs. In higher mammals or Placentals, the embryo develops in the mother's uterus, attached to an organ called the placenta. This enables the young to be nourished from the mother's bloodstream and to be born in an advanced state. Placentals include such animals as mice, bats, horses, cows, whales and monkeys.

In marsupials the placenta is either absent or very rudimentary, so that the young is born in a very immature state. From the mother's womb the tiny embryo makes its way, by instinct, upward through the mother's fur to the pouch. Inside the pouch the embryo attaches itself firmly to one of the teats which begins providing it with nourishing milk. The young remains in the pouch until it is able to leave and fend for itself.

A detailed description of the birth of kangaroos is given by H. J. Frith and J. A. Calaby in their recent book, *Kangaroos*. The newly born young is only about the size of a bean and weighs one gram. It takes only a few minutes to make the journey to the pouch. In the case of the Red Kangaroo the young lives in the pouch for an average of 235 days, though it begins leaving the pouch after 190 days and continues to be suckled for about a year after it first entered the pouch.

Habits When studying a particular animal one of the first things to consider is its habits. At what time of the day is it active? If the animal hides during the day and only comes out to feed at night it is said to be *nocturnal*. If it is active during the daylight hours and sleeps during the night it is said to be *diurnal*.

What does it eat? It may be *carnivorous* (flesh-eating,) *herbivorous* (grass-eating) or *insectivorous* (insect-eating).

Is it a *gregarious* animal (lives in groups) or is it a *solitary* species (lives by itself)? Does it live mainly on the ground (*terrestrial*) or in trees (*arboreal*)? Does it burrow, hop, leap or glide?

All these questions need to be asked when studying any particular species.

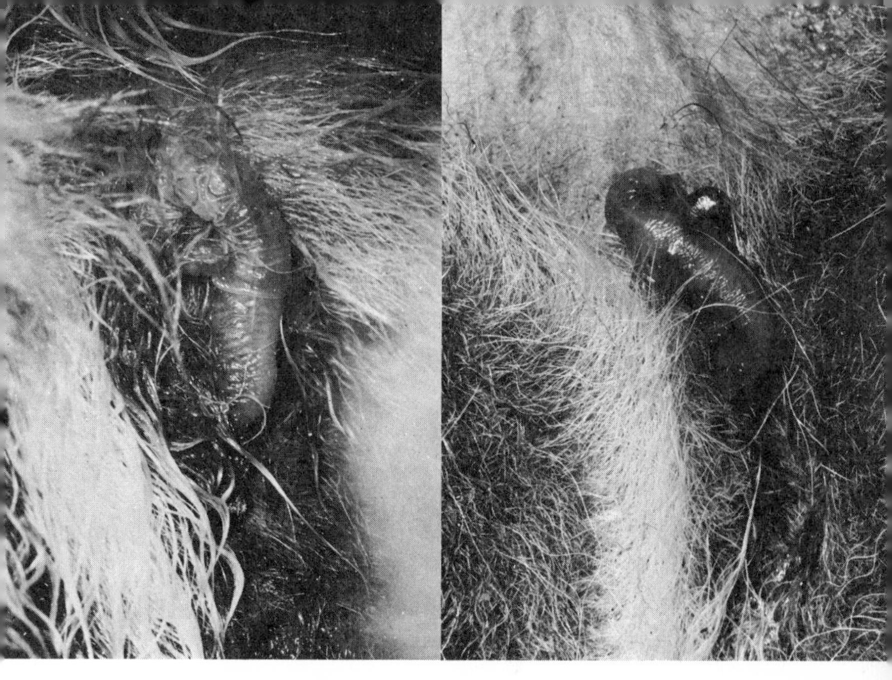

Birth of a Red Kangaroo
Top Left: Newborn young crawling from opening of womb towards the pouch.
Top Right: At the mouth of the pouch and about to enter. Below: Newborn young attached to a teat inside the pouch.

Characteristics To identify a species the scientist needs to know much more than its habits. He looks for certain characteristics which can be compared from one species to another. In the descriptions which follow, constant reference is made to these characteristics.

SIZE: Throughout the text the following approximations are used:

Minute—head and body measure less than 3½ inches.
Small—ditto 3½–6 inches.
Medium-small—ditto 7–12 inches.
Medium—ditto 13–18 inches.
Medium-large—ditto 19–24 inches.
Large—ditto 25–48 inches.
Very large—ditto more than 49 inches.

COLOUR The colour, patterns and texture of the fur are described.

DENTITION The arrangement of the animal's teeth (dentition) is an important recognition characteristic—especially when trying to identify a skeleton. The size and arrangement of the teeth vary according to the animal's diet; usually flesh-eating animals have a different dentition to those which eat only grass. The dentition also provides a guide to the relationships between different kinds of animals in the same order.

There are several other relevant characteristics, such as the pads on the soles of the feet, which are important in giving information about the animal's life. These are discussed in the descriptions.

Note Line drawings throughout the book are not to a common scale.

Top: Common Marsupial Mouse (p. 29).
Below: A Broad-footed Marsupial Mouse (p. 19)

Over page: Tiger Cat (p. 33)

▲ Dibbler (p. 22) ▼ Jerboa (p. 30) Burrow of desert marsupial ▼

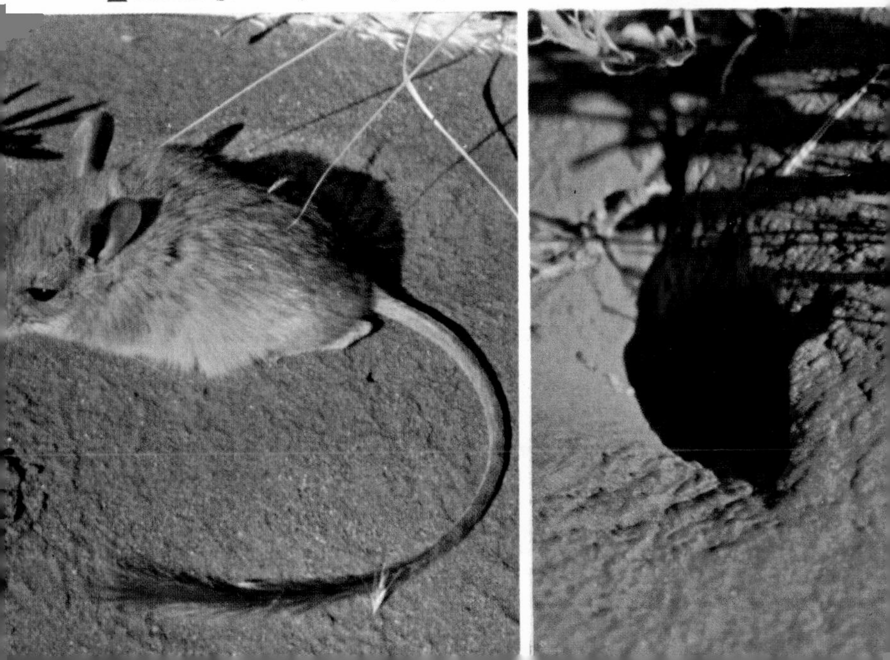

▲ Fat-tailed Marsupial Mouse (p. 27) Tasmanian Devil (p. 37) ▼

Part One

POLYPROTODONT MARSUPIALS

FAMILY DASYURIDAE

SUB-FAMILY (1) PHASCOGALINAE (Marsupial Mice)

GENUS *Antechinus* (Broad-footed Marsupial Mice)

Marsupial mice of this genus may be distinguished by a combination of two characteristics. The tail is short-haired, and the soles of the feet are short and broad, with pads transversely lined. The first toe is small and without a claw. The pouch area is not enclosed as in most other marsupials. Marsupial mice are alert, intelligent animals, active and nocturnal. They also climb, but are not strictly arboreal. Their diet consists mainly of insects and flesh—usually any creature they can overpower. Vegetable matter is sometimes eaten. Although retained here, the name "marsupial mouse" tends to be discarded by naturalists nowadays and the species are simply called phascogales.

Yellow-Footed Marsupial Mouse *Antechinus flavipes*
This is a small mouse-like marsupial with a pointed muzzle and a large rounded ear. It occurs from Cape York to Adelaide, extending inland to Cobar in NSW, and there is a distinct race, *A.f. leucogaster*, in S.W. Australia. It is grey-brown on the head and body while the undersurface is yellowish-grey. The flanks and feet are rufous (reddish), except in the paler western form.

The Yellow-footed Marsupial Mouse is commonly found in rocky areas, and in more open forests. It constructs a nest of leaves with an entrance at the back, either in rock crevices or the hollow trunks and limbs of trees. These high nests provide an effective escape from larger predators. The rigid footpads and the long claws assist this small animal in climbing.

It is solitary, mainly nocturnal, and eats insects. The mating season occurs in August and the young are born after a month, 8–12 in a litter. The pouch is absent but the edges of the area are slightly raised and contain eight teats.

Some closely related species are:

Goodman's Marsupial Mouse *A. goodmani.* From the high regions near Ravenshoe in the Cairns region of northern Queensland. It is larger, with longer snout and copper-coloured cheeks.

Harney's Marsupial Mouse *A. bilarni.* From central Australia. It is slightly smaller and lighter in colour than *flavipes*, with a longer tail.

Brown Marsupial Mouse *A. stuartii* Smaller in size than *A. flavipes* and more uniformly grey-brown in colour. It inhabits wet forests of the eastern Australian States.

Swainson's Marsupial Mouse

Swainson's Marsupial Mouse *Antechinus swainsonii*

This marsupial mouse is similar to *flavipes* except that it is larger, darker, and has a slender snout. The long foreclaws (up to 4 mm long), the darker, broader feet and much smaller ear distinguish the species. It may be found from Armidale in NSW, through Victoria to Portland, and in Tasmania. It is often found near dense vegetation along banks of streams in rain-forest or wet sclerophyll forest areas.

The sombre dark rufous-brown upper surface has an evenly speckled appearance due to the copperish-brown tipping of the fur. The undersurface is grey. The head and the body are five inches long while the tail is four inches.

Some closely related species are:

Little Tasmanian Marsupial Mouse *A. minimus*. This is a harsh-furred, brighter coloured, yellowish to reddish-grey species with longer foreclaws. It occurs in Tasmania and nearby off-shore islands, as well as a few coastal tracts of Victoria and South Australia.
Pigmy Marsupial Mouse *A. maculatus*. This is found in coastal NSW and Queensland. It is the smallest of the Broad-foot group. It was named *maculatus* by John Gould from an abherent specimen with a white streak on the throat and irregular white spots on the belly. Normal specimens have uniformly coloured underparts.
Fawn Marsupial Mouse *A. bellus*. This is a paler member with a fawn-grey upper surface, and a buff-white undersurface. The hands and feet are white above. It may be collected near the South Alligator River in the Northern Territory.

Fat-tailed Phascogale

Fat-Tailed Phascogale *Antechinus macdonnellensis*
The Fat-tailed Marsupial Mouse or Phascogale is a small mouse-like animal with a pointed muzzle and a thick tail. It is found in the Northern Territory, a large section of central Western Australia, and on Barrow Island.

It is grey-brown on the upper surface while the belly is light grey. The ear is round with a distinctive chestnut patch behind. The very fat tail is shorter than the head and the body and serves as a store of fat for lean seasons.

This animal is terrestrial, found in stony desert or rock outcrops. It comes out at night to hunt for insect food and is common over most of its range.

The pouch is shallow, with two side-folds of skin which probably develop when the six teats are occupied. The litter may be up to six. The body length ranges from three to nearly four inches, while the tail usually grows to about three inches.

Freckled Marsupial Mouse *Antechinus apicalis*

A very rare marsupial from the extreme south-west of Western Australia is the Dibbler, or Freckled Marsupial Mouse. It is small but robust in form with a pointed muzzle and short ears. The head and the body are freckled red-grey with a dull-white to yellow belly. The tail is short and tapering with longish hairs at the base and shorter black hair at the tip. The longish tail hair, which is also freckled, forms a fringe. A distinctive feature is the reddish forearms.

The Dibbler prefers sclerophyll forest, either thick or open, where it nests in hollow logs or at the base of *Xanthorrhoea* grass-trees. The nest is a raised structure of fine twigs and coarse grass, closely resembling that of the Common Long-nosed Bandicoot.

It is a ground-dweller, which comes out at night from its nest to feed on insects. The litter size may be up to eight.

The grey forefoot has five toes, each with a long claw growing to four millimetres, while the grey five-toed hindfoot has the claw missing from the first toe. The head and the body grow to a length of four and a half inches while the tail grows to three and a half inches.

GENUS *Planigale*

Flat-headed Planigale *Planigale ingrami*
These are small mouse-like creatures characterised by a flattened head with a maximum skull thickness of only one eighth of an inch. The largest species of the genus is smaller than the smallest species of the genus *Antechinus*. These are the smallest living marsupials.

Flat-headed Planigales may be found in the northern area of the Northern Territory, south to Brunette Downs and east to coastal Townsville and Mackay in Queensland. They live in savannah woodland and grassland areas where they hide under grass tussocks or in cracks in the ground. They are nocturnal, coming out to feed on insects, especially grasshoppers and crickets.

The colour of the upper surface is grey-brown with a yellowish tinge similar to a pale-coloured house mouse. The belly is lighter. The head and body are just over three inches long while the pale brown tail is two and a half inches long. The central pads on the feet are smooth, not serrated, reflecting the terrestrial habits of the genus.

They are solitary, or occur in small groups. The males are particularly active and run swiftly to cover if disturbed, while the females are quieter and more timid. When carrying young they are almost incapacitated by the large load. Litter size varies from four to six, and birth occurs in January in the Northern Territory.

The **Southern** or **Dusky Planigale** *P. tenuirostris* may be found in northern NSW and southern Queensland. It is darker in colour and has a narrower muzzle than *ingrami*.

GENUS *Phascogale*

Brush-tailed Phascogale *Phascogale tapoatafa*
This is the largest of the Broad-foot species and can be distinguished by a brush of long black hairs round the terminal three-quarters of the tail. This animal is a beautiful blue-grey with a pale grey belly.

The Brush-tailed Phascogale extends in range from southern Queensland, through eastern NSW to Victoria. Other groups may be found in Arnhem Land and south-western Western Australia. It prefers sclerophyll forest and woodland.

These animals have the reputation of being very bloodthirsty. Many farmers have disturbed them in chicken roosts slaying poultry. If captured, the Brush-tailed Phascogale can be extremely ferocious and will struggle hard to escape, sometimes lacerating the captor. Even though it can sometimes prove to be rather a nuisance, it is also of great value in preying upon rats and mice. There have been reports that the Brush-tailed Phascogale has followed plagues of rodents, thinning them out.

This animal grows to seventeen inches long including the tail. It is solitary in habits, nocturnal and semi-arboreal. In the wild it feeds almost entirely on large insects. It builds a nest of leaves in the hollow of a tree and has a litter of about eight.

The **Red-tailed Phascogale** *P. calura*, from the south-west corner of Western Australia is a closely related species, being smaller and redder.

GENUS *Dasycercus*

Crest-tailed Marsupial Mouse *Dasycercus cristicauda*
Also called the Mulgara, this is one of the most fearless and intelligent of our marsupials. It is small but robust. The muzzle is pointed, while the ears are short and rounded. The head and body are sandy or reddish-brown, and the belly is pure white. The tail is tapered and tipped at the end with a crest of black hairs running from the upper surface to the lower surface.

The Crest-tailed Marsupial Mouse may be found from central Northern Territory south through South Australia into Western Australia. Another race occurs east of Lake Eyre. It prefers a habitat of stony or spinifex desert where it lives in burrows. Unlike other mammals, it is not necessarily nocturnal, and comes out during the day to bask in the sun. It is a social, active animal which eats insects and small vertebrates such as rodents. In capacity it will quickly kill a large mouse, eating it from head to tail with medical precision and turning the skin inside out.

In South Australia Mulgaras breed between June and September. They usually have a litter of six to eight. The pouch is nearly absent and the small young are only protected by a shallow ridge of skin, where they cling to the teats. These animals are normally scarce, but can become plentiful after a good season.

The **Western Crest-tailed Marsupial Mouse** *D. blythi*, is a close relation from two areas in north-western Western Australia near the Pilbara region. It is lighter in colour with a grey base to the fur.

Byrne's Marsupial Mouse *Dasycercus byrnei*
This is a most unusual marsupial from the region of the Simpson Desert at the junction of South Australia, Queensland and the Northern Territory, in central Australia. It is medium-small, and robust in form. It has a pointed muzzle, and short round ears. The body is reddish-grey while the belly is white. The tail is rufous at the base with a black brush. The hind foot lacks the first toe.

These desert-dwelling animals live in burrows on sandy or stony ground and come out at night to feed on insects, small mammals and reptiles. The pouch is only slightly developed, consisting of two side folds enclosing six teats. The young are born after a gestation period of thirty-two days and are only 4 mm long. Byrne's Marsupial Mice mature after twelve months. The species was first discovered by the Horn Expedition to central Australia in 1894.

GENUS *Sminthopsis* (Narrow-footed Marsupial Mice)

This genus contains those marsupial mice distinguished from the broad-footed marsupial mice by the slenderness of their feet, and by having narrow hind-soles occasionally partly-haired. The pads are reduced to granulated areas found at the base of the toes. Generally the ears are large and the pouch is more developed and the tail thicker than the broad-footed species.

Narrow-footed marsupial mice live in burrows, among rocks, or hidden in logs and fallen limbs or debris. They are insectivorous, but occasionally become carnivorous. In favourable seasons the female may have up to ten youngsters. The common names "marsupial mouse" and sminthopsis are not now favoured by most naturalists, who use "dunnart" instead.

Fat-tailed Marsupial Mouse *Sminthopsis crassicaudata*

The Fat-tailed Marsupial Mouse is a small mouse-like marsupial with a pointed muzzle, a spindle-shaped tail shorter than the body, large oval-shaped ears, and a dark-coloured triangle marking on top of the head. It occurs across inland NSW from the Dividing Range to Lake Eyre in central Australia, south to the Victorian and South Australian coast. It also may be found in the south-west of Western Australia. It prefers a habitat of savannah woodland and grassland where it may be found hiding under stumps and inside decayed fence posts. It also occurs in salt-bush country.

Generally the Fat-tailed Marsupial Mouse is less active than any species of *Antechinus*, being nocturnal and terrestrial in habits. It occurs singly or in pairs. It feeds on insects and relishes grasshoppers.

Other related species are:

Darling Downs Sminthopsis *S. macrura*, found on the Liverpool Range plains area on northern NSW and the Darling Downs region of south-eastern Queensland. It is larger than *crassicaudata*, with a longer, less fattened and tapering tail. The ears are shorter, and the sole pads have coarser granulations. The greyish general colour and the thicker tail-base distinguish *macrura* from the sandy-buff *larapinta* of western Queensland.

Stripe-headed Sminthopsis *S. larapinta*, found near the Lake Eyre basin extending across central Australia into Western Queensland. It may be distinguished from *crassicaudata* and *murina* by the greater length of the tail and the greater thickening of the tail base. It also has a distinct stripe on the forehead and long feet. It is terrestrial, lives in burrows, and prefers stony tablelands to softer ground.

Granule-footed Sminthopsis *S. granulipes*, occurs in south-Western Australia. This species may be distinguished by its thinner white tail. The ears are shorter and broader as well as being distinctive in shape. The main features are the rasp-like granulations on the fore and hind feet.

Hairy-footed Sminthopsis *S. hirtipes*, occurs in the Northern Territory extending into Western Australia. It may be distinguished by its palms which are covered by an odd-shaped cushion covered with silky hairs. At the base of the toes is an elevation not divided into pads. A fringe of hairs occur on the outer edge of the feet. The long tail is dull white and the half near the body is only slightly thickened.

Common Marsupial Mouse *Sminthopsis murina*
A small mouse-like marsupial very similar in form to *Sminthopsis crassicaudata*. It is distinguished by a longer, tapering, more slender tail. Its colour is brownish, while the belly is grey-white. Common Marsupial Mice may be found singly or in pairs throughout their range. They are terrestrial and live on a diet of insects. They occur in dry sclerophyll forest or woodland where they nest in hollow logs or under sheets of bark. The litter may comprise as many as eight.

Sminthopsis murina extends in range from Cooktown in Queensland, through inland New South Wales, to western Victoria and South Australia, and then across to far south-western Australia.

The sole pads of *murina* are characterised by a row of beaded granules along the base of each pad. As the pads wear down, the divisions may appear as serrations, so that the species may be mistaken for *S. leucopus*. Some closely related species are:

White-footed Marsupial Mouse *S. leucopus*, is a uniform dark greyish brown above, with a darker tail and clear white feet from which its specific name derives. The foot pads of this species are serrated.

Rufous-cheeked Marsupial Mouse *S. rufigenis*, occurs in New Guinea and across tropical Australia. It is distinguished by rufous cheeks.

Long-tailed Marsupial Mouse *S. longicaudata*, occurs in arid north-west Western Australia near the Pilbara region. It has a long tail twice the length of its head and body. Its colour is grey tinged with red. The forearm, hand and foot are white.

GENUS *Antechinomys* (Jerboa Marsupial Mice)

Australia's Jerboa Marsupial Mice are *Sminthopsis*-like in form, but have elongated fore- and hind-limbs as well as a long tail, tufted at the tip. For many years it was believed that they progressed in a hopping manner similar to a kangaroo, but recently it has been found that they run rapidly on four legs. Like most other animals of their size, they are insectivorous, but may also eat small rodents and lizards. Many books state that the pouch is absent, but in the British Museum there is a specimen with a clearly developed pouch with a flap of skin at the front and at the sides. The opening is directed backward.

Very little is known of the breeding habits, but up to six young have been recorded in a litter.

Jerboa Marsupial Mouse *Antechinomys spenceri*
This is a small, delicate, dull sandy-brown marsupial with a long crested tail. It may be found from western WA, through NT and SA into western Queensland. It may be found in sandy or desert grassland as well as desert steppe. It lives beneath spinifex tussocks or saltbush in a burrow often shared or borrowed from kangaroo-mice or other rodents.

It is solitary, a ground-dweller and nocturnal. It has very long ears, oval in shape, and very long hindfeet with a very large, pale cushion-like pad. The forelimbs have five toes, while the hindlimbs have only four. The animals can be distinguished from rodents by possessing many incisor teeth, instead of a pair above and a pair below as rodents have.

The **Eastern Jerboa Marsupial Mouse** *A. laniger*, is a close relation found in the interior of NSW and southern Queensland. This marsupial is dark grey and is smaller than the central form. It can be distinguished by the dark soles on its hindfeet. It now seems to be very rare over most of its range.

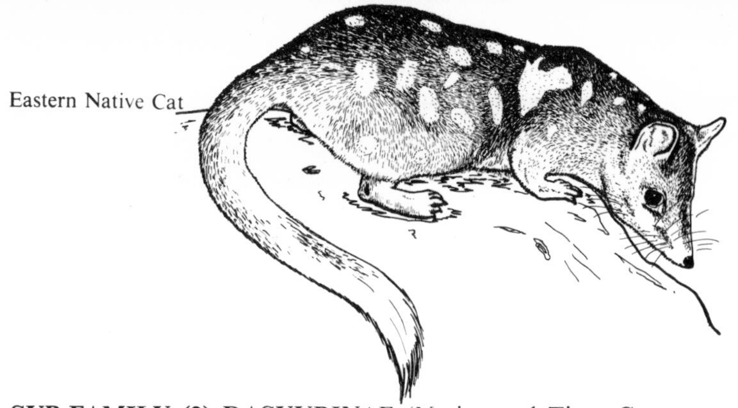

SUB-FAMILY (2) DASYURINAE (Native and Tiger Cats, Tasmanian Devil)

This sub-family contains the medium-sized, carnivorous, spotted marsupials known as Native Cats, and the Tasmanian Devil, which is similar in form to a small bear. A characteristic which shows the evolutionary link between Native Cats and the Tasmanian Devil is the arrangement of their teeth, which are adapted to a diet of flesh. They have two premolars on each side, above and below, while the Tasmanian Wolf has three premolars on each side. Other features which show their affinity are the similar ears, muzzles, and palm and sole-pads. Native cats are sometimes arboreal, while the Devil is always terrestrial.

GENUS *Dasyurus* (Native Cats)

Eastern Native Cat *Dasyurus viverrinus*
The Eastern Native Cat originally occurred about the east coast of Australia from Armidale through NSW and Victoria to Tasmania and South Australia. It lived in dry sclerophyll forest sheltering in hollow limbs and among rocks. It is a fearless animal, with a great deal of intelligence. It is nocturnal and feeds on insects, small rodents and marsupials, birds and lizards.

The Eastern Native Cat is olive-grey spotted with white, with a pale grey undersurface. The tail is unspotted and has a white tip. Another colour phase—black with white spots, with a black tipped tail—also occurs. The Eastern Native Cat may be distinguished from the Tiger Cat by the lack of spots on the tail, and by possessing only four hind toes instead of five. The pouch may be absent or well developed, but is stimulated to growth prior to the birth of young. As many as twenty-four young have been born to the Eastern Native Cat, but there are only eight teats to feed the young. The gestation

Northern Native Cat

period is quite short, only fourteen days. The young are independent at about four-and-a-half months old.

Together with many other marsupials, Native Cats were decimated by an epidemic disease in 1901–3 and the species became very rare over most of its range. It may even be extinct in Australia, although it is common in Tasmania.

Northern Native Cat *Dasyurus hallucatus*
This species is the smallest of the native cats and may be found mainly in tropical regions across the north of Australia, especially along the coast. It prefers to live in hollow logs or outcroppings of rock in open woodland and desert grassland. Compared with the Eastern Native Cat and the Western Native Cat the hair is shorter and more coarse, with thin under-fur. The colour is a more dusky yellowish-brown on the upper surface, covered with white spots. The undersurface and feet are yellowish or drab white. The large, leafy, thin ear is sparsely covered with fine hairs. The tail of the Northern Native Cat is long, but not as long as the Western Native Cat, and is short-haired, unspotted, and black at the tip. There are five toes on the fore- and hind-feet each—except the first toes on the hindfeet—has a claw. The Northern Native Cat is a solitary animal and an active climber. Because of this it has well-defined serrated pads on the palms and soles of the feet. It is nocturnal and feeds on insects, small mammals and lizards. The litter may contain as many as eight.

Tiger Cat *Dasyurus maculatus*

The Tiger Cat is a large carnivorous, plucky animal with a powerful build and a fairly blunt muzzle. The body is dark brown while the belly is pale yellow. Both the body and the tail are spotted with large white disks.

This animal may be found in coastal regions of eastern Australia from Cooktown in Queensland, south to Victoria and perhaps South Australia. It is uncommon on the mainland but is plentiful in Tasmania. It prefers the more wooded districts of the coast and nearby mountains in rain-forest and wet sclerophyll forest. Here it shelters in hollow logs and among rocks in rock piles. As indicated by its serrated foot pads, it is a tree-dweller.

The Tiger Cat is a solitary animal, coming out during the night to feed on small mammals and birds. In Victoria birth may occur in May and the litter contains as many as six. The pouch is a concentric flap of skin enclosing the front and sides of the mammary region. There are six teats.

Western Native Cat *Dasyurus geoffroii*

The Western Native Cat was once found in New South Wales west of the Dividing Range, in Queensland, Northern Territory, Victoria, South Australia and Western Australia. It is now probably extinct in all these States except for the south-west area of Western Australia slightly inland from the coast, where it is still common.

It is about the same size as the Eastern Native Cat, but is slightly more robust. It can be distinguished by its longer, but less bushy tail, which is tipped with black extending back along the greater part of the underside, and by having a distinct first toe on the hindfoot. The soles on the feet lack serrations indicating the animal's habits are not arboreal. In other ways the animal is similar to the Northern Native Cat.

Tasmanian Devil

▲ Numbat (p. 38)

Short-nosed Bandicoot (p. 41) ▼

GENUS *Sarcophilus*

Tasmanian Devil *Sarcophilus harrisi*

This large, powerfully-built creature was the first mammal observed by the early settlers in Van Dieman's Land, and its fierce expression, snarling growl, and black colour earned it the name of Devil or Native Devil. Even now it is still common in Tasmania, especially in the centre, while skeletal remains may also be found on the mainland. It favours fairly open forest country, sheltering in rock piles and hollow logs. It comes out at night to hunt.

The Tasmanian Devil is a powerful carnivore which feeds on medium-sized animals and birds. It has a robust build with a short, broad muzzle, and short, rounded ears. Black is the general colour, with one white band across the chest, while another may occur across the rump. The tail is black and evenly haired. The forefeet have five toes while the hindfeet have only four toes. Each toe is very strongly clawed. The head and the body grow to a length of about twenty-eight inches while the tail is only twelve inches long

Although they have a black reputation, Tasmanian Devils make delightful pets when reared in captivity and are quite affectionate. They are clean animals which 'wash' themselves with cupped hands; they love to bathe and bask in the sun. Although they are essentially ground-dwellers, they can also climb competently.

Mating occurs between March and April and the gestation period lasts about thirty-one days. The litter may contain as many as four. The pouch consists of a horseshoe flap of skin, fading out at the rear, so that it is directed backwards. There are two pairs of teats.

◀ Honey Possum (p. 51)

SUB-FAMILY (3) MYRMECOBIINAE (Marsupial Ant-eater)

The Marsupial Ant-eater is classified as a separate subfamily containing a single species. It can be distinguished by its small, flattened, slender form; its barred colouration and brushy tail, and the arrangement of its teeth, which are modified to suit a white-ant diet. The tongue is four inches long and cylindrical. When the animal is feeding, it flicks out in all directions into termite-riddled timber. The termites are generally swallowed whole, except for the heavy-jawed workers which are subjected to rapid and audible chewing.

GENUS *Myrmecobius*

Marsupial Ant-eater or **Numbat** *Myrmecobius fasciatus*
The Banded Ant-eater is reddish-brown, with darker colouring on the rump; the belly is sandy-brown. A feature which readily distinguishes this animal from all others is the six white bars which cross the rump. A dark stripe runs through the eye. In size it is similar to a large rat, with the brushy tail giving it a squirrel-like appearance, but the sharply pointed snout is not typical of rodents.

The range of this animal is fairly restricted. In Western Australia it occurs from one hundred miles north of Perth, south to Albany. Another specimen was taken at Coolgardie. It is found in open dry sclerophyll forest where it shelters in hollow logs. Unlike most other marsupials, the Marsupial Ant-eater is not nocturnal, but moves about during the day. It hurries about in a series of leaps similar to a trotting action in slow motion. It does not burrow at any time, but can be quite an agile climber.

A closely related form is the South Australian **South-eastern** or **Rusty Numbat** *M. fasciatus rufus*. It is a richer red colour, especially on the crown and foreparts, which are touched with white hairs instead of black. It was once widely distributed in South Australia across to western New South Wales. It may now be extinct.

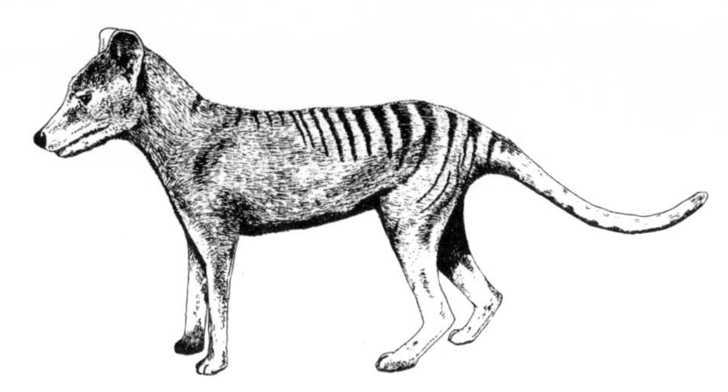

FAMILY THYLACINIDAE (Tasmanian Wolf)

The structure of the muzzle, ear and paws is essentially that of the Dasyuridae, and the pouch is identical with that of the Tasmanian Devil.

GENUS *Thylacinus*

Tasmanian Wolf or **Thylacine** *Thylacinus cynocephalus*
The Tasmanian Wolf is the most interesting of the flesh-eating marsupials, but is now extremely rare, if not extinct. It was once found on the mainland (as shown by fossil remains in caves) but was confined to Tasmania before the advent of white man. The last specimen collected for science was caught over forty years ago, but foot prints were noted in southern Tasmania in 1957.

The animal is large and dog-like, with a long, pointed muzzle and short round ears. The body colour is grey-brown and the belly light yellow-brown. On the back there are about sixteen transverse bars extending from the shoulders to the tail. These dark brown bars are widest on the rump. There are five toes on the forefeet and four on the hindfeet. This animal grows to about five feet in length including the tail, which grows to twenty inches.

Most of the time the Tasmanian Wolf dwells in rocky lairs, roaming at dusk in search of prey, which includes small wallabies, birds, mammals and lizards. Generally it is solitary or runs in pairs. This marsupial provides a remarkable example of parallelism, being very dog-like in a number of features. It has long canine teeth for grabbing and killing, while the pre-molars are designed for shearing flesh and molars crush the bones. The skull is similar to a dog's. It is not as speedy as a dog, but wears its prey out by constant tracking.

FAMILY NOTORYCTIDAE (Marsupial Moles)

Marsupial Moles are very similar in form to the African Golden Moles. This similarity is caused by their adaption to a burrowing environment, for the animals are not remotely related.

The snout of the Marsupial Mole is protected by a horny shield, and the eyes have degenerated into lens-like internal discs. Where the ear lobe should be found, only a small opening occurs beneath the fur. The tail is rudimentary and covered with leathery skin, while the pouch opens backwards. The stout limbs are highly modified for digging: the third and fourth fingernails are greatly enlarged, forming a shovel-like organ which is used for digging and to throw up sand behind. The Marsupial Mole is so specialised in form that its relationship with other marsupials is in doubt, but certain features indicate a possible early link with the Bandicoots.

GENUS *Notoryctes*

Marsupial Mole *Notoryctes typhlops*

This animal is the most specialised and highly adapted of our marsupials in Australia. It has evolved totally as a burrower, with rudimentary eyes, no external ears, an extremely hard snout, a short horny tail and large clawed limbs for digging. It may be found in the southern area of the Northern Territory, extending south to the Great Australian Bight. It occurs in sand-ridge country capped with mulga, saltbush or spinifex.

The Marsupial Mole is a solitary animal. It burrows under the sand in shallow tunnels, coming to the surface every few feet to breathe. On the surface it shuffles along leaving a most unusual triple track. When it goes back to burrowing, its snout bores in and the claws soon dig the animal back under the surface. Its path may often be followed, for the sand falls in on its temporary tunnel. A number of observers have said that this animal can easily be tracked after rain. It feeds mainly on insects, and breeds in November; the litter is one or two. It is said to be uncommon, but lack of observations may be due to its excellent camouflage and secretive behaviour.

Another closely related species is the **North-western Marsupial Mole** *Notoryctes caurinus*. This smaller pinkish-cinnamon Marsupial Mole occurs in north-western Western Australia and appears to be rather rare.

Marsupial Mole

FAMILY PERAMELIDAE (Australian Bandicoots)

Bandicoots possess the polyprotodont teeth arrangement of the preceding insect- and flesh-eating families, and the foot structure of the diprotodont kangaroos and possums. The foot structure includes the jointed small second and third toes which appear as one, with only the last joints and claws being free. This twin toe is used as a highly efficient hair-comb toilet implement. Bandicoots are well known for their infestations of ticks and mites, and this may be why they evolved the unusual foot structure.

The diet of Bandicoots is varied. Some are mixed feeders, while others are either vegetarian or carnivorous. They have earned a bad name with many gardeners because of the damage they do to plants while digging pits in search of insects among roots.

GENUS *Isoodon* (Short-nosed Bandicoots)

Although a long snout is a characteristic of bandicoots the snout of the Short-nosed Bandicoot is stouter and shorter than that of other species. The animals are sturdy, compact, and harsh-coated, with comparatively short rounded ears and coarsely granulated soles.

Short-nosed Bandicoot *Isoodon obesulus*

Short-nosed Bandicoots are solitary ground dwellers. They nest under grass tussocks or piles of debris and come out at night to feed on insect larvae which they dig from the ground with their long snouts and powerful foreclaws. They are found in open forest, or woodland, often bordering on cultivated areas. According to present classification *I. obesulus* comprises a number of forms widely

Short-nosed Bandicoot

scattered about the Australian mainland, on off-shore islands and in Tasmania.

Other closely related species are:

Brindled Bandicoot *I. macrourus macrourus.* Found across the northern region of the Northern Territory. It is similar to *I. obesulus* except that it is much larger with a long tail. It is the largest of the genus *Isoodon.*

Giant Brindled Bandicoot *I. m. torosus.* Extends from Cape York south along the coastal strip to the Clarence River in NSW. It is common throughout its range. It may grow up to twenty-six inches from the head to the tail tip. Its range overlaps widely that of the Long-nosed Bandicoot, from which it can be distinguished by its stouter snout, shorter rounder ears, and blackish-yellow brindling on the upper surface.

Long-nosed Bandicoot

GENUS *Perameles* (Slender or Long-nosed Bandicoots)

Members of this genus are lighter and more graceful than the Short-nosed Bandicoots, with longer and more tapered snouts. The coat is finer, smoother, and less grizzled in colour. The ears are also longer and more pointed while the hind half of the sole is hairy, not smooth. Except for the common eastern species and one Central Australian form, a barred marking on the upper surface is characteristic.

Long-Nosed Bandicoot *Perameles nasuta*
This species is the second largest bandicoot on the mainland. It is very numerous about Sydney being accused of causing damage to suburban gardens and lawns. Its conical pits are dug while it is searching for insects and larvae amongst roots.

In form, the animals are medium-sized and slender. They have a long pointed muzzle and a long ear with a pointed tip. The fur is olive-brown while the belly is white. The tail is short and tapering. They grow to about twenty inches in length, including the five-inch tail. The animals are solitary in habit, ground-dwelling and nocturnal. They breed throughout the year, usually with three or four to a litter. The Long-nosed Bandicoot may be found down the coastal strip and eastern highlands of Australia from Cape York to south-western Victoria. It occurs in both rain forest and sclerophyll forest, where it shelters under debris.

Some barred relations of the Long-nosed Bandicoot are:
Tasmanian Barred Bandicoot *P. gunnii.* Largest of the barred Perameles. The tail is short and slender, mainly white. It is common in the northern parts of Tasmania, off-shore islands and occurs in western Victoria.
Little Marl or **Barred Bandicoot** *P. bougainville.* A rather elegant species usually with a brightly coloured, dark barred, rump and a brown tail. It is nocturnal, seeking shelter during the day in hollow logs or under stones, sometimes constructing a crude nest. In some forms the bars on the rump are indistinct. It occurs in Western Australia but was originally in South Australia and inland New South Wales too.

GENUS *Macrotis* (Bilbies or Rabbit-eared Bandicoots)

These are most beautiful animals with long silky, blue-grey fur, long rabbit-like ears, and a long tri-coloured, well-haired tail. The molar teeth are large and broad and in the adults are often worn to a smooth surface, as in other bandicoots.

Rabbit-eared Bandicoots are the only bandicoots to excavate tunnels for occupation. Their powerfully-clawed forearms make them expert tunnellers. The burrow does not have a second exit, but if it is being dug out by a hunter, the Rabbit-eared Bandicoot can easily dig faster than a man with a shovel.

The Bilby was once widespread, but its range has been drastically reduced by human settlement and introduced foxes.

Rabbit-eared Bandicoot or **Bilby** *Macrotis lagotis*

This species is distinguished from the smaller one by the black basal band completely encircling the tail, instead of being on top of the tail or faint or absent as in *M. minor*. The size of this species varies according to local conditions and previous seasons, but is generally that of a full-grown rabbit.

Rabbit-eared Bandicoots live in open woodland or shrub steppe where they live in burrows. They tend to live in pairs and eat insects and small vertebrates. In South Australia births may occur from March to May. The litter is two.

Originally the species ranged through the drier parts of temperate Australia, from north-eastern New South Wales to the far south-west. The eastern populations are evidently extinct now.

The related species is the **Lesser Rabbit-eared Bandicoot**. A dark species, sombre blackish-grey or warmish chestnut-grey in colour. The fur on the belly is dark grey, not white. It occurs in a small area near the NT, Qld and SA border.

▲ Pigmy Possum (p. 55) Squirrel Glider (p. 60) ▼

▲ Sugar Glider (p. 60)

Green Ringtail Possum (p. 62) ▶

▼ Golden Brush-tailed Possum (p. 64)

Western Ringtail Possum (p. 62) ▼

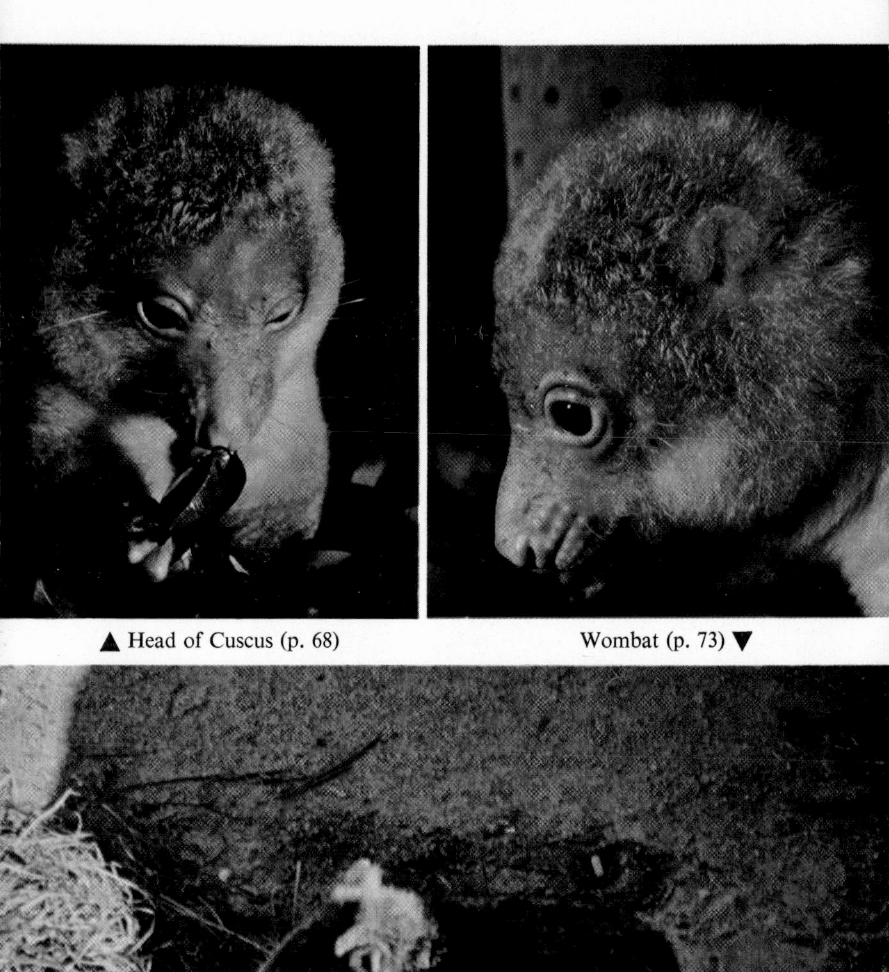

▲ Head of Cuscus (p. 68)

Wombat (p. 73) ▼

GENUS *Chaeropus* (Pig-footed Bandicoots)

This interesting genus is represented by one species, found originally from the Murray River area of eastern Australia to southern Western Australia. Aside from the unusual appearance, the foot structure identifies this group. The first and fifth toes have gone, the fourth is rudimentary, and the strongly-clawed second and third digits form a cleft hoof. This may be an adaption for running.

Pig-footed Bandicoot *Chaeropus ecaudatus ecaudatus*
This species ranged widely in South Australia occurring mainly on shrub–steppe plains where it nested under salt-bushes. It was partly diurnal, and was said to squat in the open with its ears laid back like a rabbit's. When chased it would run to the shelter of hollow logs or trees. As with many marsupials, its habit of sheltering in timber made it a victim of bushfires, while flocks of sheep have long ago banished it from settlement. With the introduction of the fox its fate may now be sealed. It may now be extinct.

Pig-footed Bandicoots are medium-small and slender. They have a very long snout and a broad head which has been likened to the narrow neck of a broad bottle. The body is fawn-grey and the belly is white. The tail is crested with black on the upper and lower surface. This species is said to be a mixed feeder. When Surveyor-General Major Mitchell discovered the species, the original specimen was without a tail, hence the Latin name *ecaudatus*.

Part Two

DIPROTODONT MARSUPIALS

In the second of the two great divisions of the Marsupialia, members are characterised by having not more than three front (incisor) teeth on each side of the upper jaw, and normally there is only one functional incisor on each side of the lower jaw.

The Diprotodonts are divided into four families:

1. Phalangeridae, the tree–dwelling possoms
2. Phascolarctidae, sole living representative the Koala
3. Vombatidae, the wombats
4. Macropodidae (great-footed), the kangaroos and their allies

One characteristic is the peculiar modification of the hindfoot in which the second and third toes are more-or-less joined together. The united toes and the pair of large lower incisors distinguish all the members of this group.

FAMILY PHALANGERIDAE (Possums and Cuscus)

The possums are mainly tree dwellers. They feed either upon insects, as did their ancestors, or upon blossoms, foliage or nectar from the trees in which they live.

Possums usually have long prehensile tails (capable of grasping), sometimes underlain by a strip of naked skin used for gripping branches, or well-furred to assist gliding. They also have strong sharp claws, with an opposing thumb to grip branches while climbing. The second and third toes are united, and the twin claws act as preening combs. The pouch is well formed and opens forwards; it contains two to six teats. Some small mouse-like possums have teeth suited for eating insects while their limbs and tail are suited to life in trees.

Several unrelated genera have evolved gliding membranes, and strongly brushed tails which act as rudders for gliding. Other genera have evolved prehensile tails. Possums are not capable of sustained flight but make a gliding descent (known as volplaning) from higher branches to lower parts of a nearby tree or the ground.

GENUS *Tarsipes* (Honey Possum)

This possum is so distinctive that its close relations are untraceable. The Honey Possum is readily distinguished by having three dark brown stripes along the back, a long trunk-like snout, and a long prehensile tail. The snout is used for thrusting into blossoms and around bottle-brush cones. The tongue is also able to curl round and channel the nectar from the flower. This tongue is bristly at the tip, able to pick up sticky food from the flowers. The teeth are extremely degenerate, having become adapted to a honey diet, which requires no mastication. Only the soft bodies of insects are chewed.

Honey Possum *Tarsipes spenserae*
This minute, slender animal is confined to the south-west coastal district of Western Australia. It is to be found mainly in tea-tree scrub or bottle-brush scrub. Here it builds a nest of grass amongst branches, and raises up to four young. It is generally solitary or occurs in pairs. It is an active climber, coming out at night to feed. Due to its small size and nocturnal life it is rarely seen, but still seems to be reasonably common about Perth.

Honey Possums are said to move about in colonies from one area to another, according to the availability of flowers, especially varieties which bloom all the year round. Their agility is quite remarkable; they are able to hang upside down by their tails while feeding.

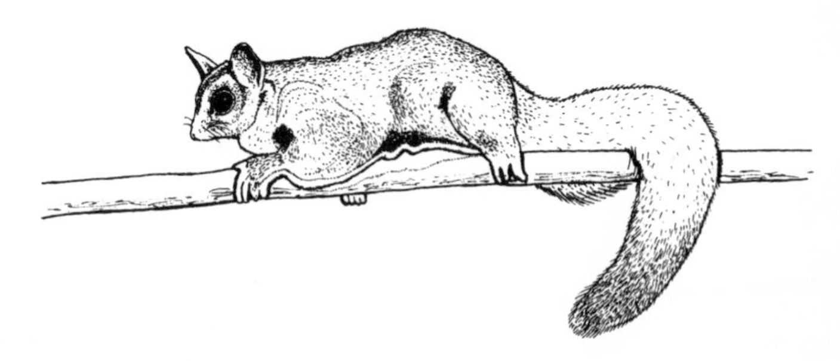

Pigmy Glider

GENUS *Acrobates*

Pigmy or **Feather-tail Glider** *Acrobates pygmaeus*

The Pigmy Glider is very small and mouse-like in form, with a short muzzle and rounded ears. The head and the body are greyish-brown while the belly is whitish, with a grey base to the fur.

This is the smallest marsupial adapted for gliding flight, and can readily be identified by its side flaps and by a feather-like tail with a row of hairs on each side. It is quite common in eastern Australia but is rarely seen because of its nocturnal and furtive habits. The gliding flights of this little possum are really prolonged leaps aided by the parachute effect of the membranes between the limbs and the feather tail, which acts as a rudder. Food consists of both insects and nectar.

The animals are to be found in both woodland and sclerophyll forest, where they nest in small groups in knot-holes or hollow limbs. The globular nest is formed of gum leaves and often includes shredded bark. The litter may contain as many as four.

The species is distributed from Cape York in Queensland to New South Wales and Victoria.

Pigmy Possum

Greater Glider Possum (p. 61) ▶

Top: Red-legged Pademelon (p. 94). Below: Rufous Rat-kangaroo (p. 80)

GENUS *Cercartetus* (Dormouse or Pigmy Possums)

These delightful little possums were once grouped under two genera, *Cercartetus* and *Eudromicia*, but are now combined in the genus *Cercartetus*. To the early settlers their sleeping, eating and living habits were very similar to the rodent dormice of Europe, even though they are not related.

These small possums are amongst the most primitive of the family Phalangeridae and in form are very similar to the insectivorous prototypes.

Dormouse or **Pigmy Possum** *Cercartetus nanus*
This small, robust species was first described from Tasmania. It is found also in south-eastern Australia from SE. Queensland to Mt. Gambier SA. It prefers dry sclerophyll forest regions where it lives amongst the lower shrubbery.

The woolly fur is grey-brown on the head and body, while the belly is greyish-white. The prehensile tail is long and tapering and the head is short and conical. The Pigmy Possum is a common, nocturnal tree-dweller, feeding mainly on insects and nectar. It spends the day coiled up in bark nests in hollow branches. In summer this animal is slender and mouse-like but as winter approaches the tail and body become fattened. This food store is consumed when the animal becomes torpid in the colder months. The Pigmy Possum breeds at any time during the year, producing four young at once.

There are three other species:

C. lepidus occurs in Tasmania. It is smaller. The upper surface is fawn-brown while the lower surface is greyish white. Its habits are similar to those of *nanus*. Has a row of four molars.

C. caudatus occurs on the Atherton–Herberton tableland in NE. Queensland in tropical rainforest and scrubs. Has a row of four molars. Rich brown above, cream-white below. Has longer more slender tail. Is also found in Papua. The head and body combined measure four inches.

C. concinnus, the **Mundarda**, is very small, fawn-brown in general colour with the belly-fur pure white. It occurs in woodland and scrublands of south-western WA, south-eastern SA and western Victoria.

GENUS *Dactylopsila* (Striped Possum)

The scientific name *Dactylopsila* refers to the naked-looking digits on the hands and the feet of the black and white Striped Possum. Other conspicuous features are the long fourth fingers, and the powerful incisor teeth, both used for digging grubs out of timber.

Striped Possum *Dactylopsila trivirgata*
The medium-small Striped Possum is a highly adapted marsupial found in the coastal scrubs and mountain rainforests of northern Queensland north of Townsville. It has heavy black-and-white stripes like a skunk, with a pale yellow belly. It also possesses a rather offensive smell, which may be to deter predators. The long fourth finger is for extracting grubs from under bark or cracks in timber. It will also eat other insects.

Striped Possums are solitary animals, spending much of their time in trees moving smoothly from branch to branch with a flowing motion. Their main food is wood-boring grubs which are detected by a rapid thumping of the hand on the branch to disturb the insect underneath. It is then ferreted out by smell and strength, the hands and incisors ripping off the bark and wood with great force. During the day the possums sleep in a hollow limb or in a nest constructed in the branch of a tree.

▲ Koala (p. 68)

▲ Parma Wallabies (p. 101)

Head of Pretty-face Wallaby (p. 96) ▼

▲ Albino Wallaby
▲ Potoroo (p. 81)

Lumholtz's Tree Kangaroo (p. 89) ▼

GENUS *Gymnobelideus* (Leadbeater's Possum)

The only species of this genus is extremely rare and may only be found in southern Victoria in isolated pockets in wet sclerophyll areas. No specimens were found after 1909 and it was regarded as extinct, but in 1961 one was found in the Maryville region, and since then occasional Leadbeater's Possums have been found.

Leadbeater's Possum *Gymnobelideus leadbeateri*
Except for the absence of gliding membranes this rare possum closely resembles the Sugar Glider. A feature which is common to both is a dark brown-to-blackish stripe which runs along the back from the head and upper back. The tail is long and bushy, sometimes blackish towards the tip.

This small possum is arboreal and nocturnal. Because it is so rare little is known of its biology and habits. Its tooth structure seems to suggest that it eats both insects and nectar.

GENUS *Petaurus* (Lesser Gliding Possums)

Members of this most attractive genus have parachute-like gliding membranes and long bushy tails to glide and guide themselves in the air when leaping from higher branches to lower branches. They possess the semi-insectivorous dentition of the non-gliding pigmy possum group.

Sugar Glider *Petaurus breviceps*
This species extends from the Northern Territory through Cape York south through coastal NSW and Victoria to enter South Australia. It extends inland to the western slopes of the Dividing Range in NSW. The Sugar Glider is common over most of its range. It is a small active animal living in small groups in sclerophyll forests or woodlands where it can be found nesting in hollow branches. It is arboreal and nocturnal. It feeds on both insects and nectar from blossoms of eucalypts and shrubs. The season of birth is variable and the litter is two. The **Squirrel Glider** *Petaurus norfolcensis* occurs from central coastal Queensland through NSW to Victoria. It is found in central NSW. It is larger than the Sugar Glider, the head and the body being about ten inches long, with a white belly and a more distinct black dorsal line on the upper surface.

Yellow-bellied Glider *Petaurus australis*
This glider, the largest member of its genus, occurs from the NSW–Qld border south through mountainous sclerophyll forest country to Portland in Victoria. It nests in hollow branches. Another sub-species occurs from the NSW–Qld border north to Bundaberg and in an isolated region near Mt. Spurgeon near Cairns.

It is grey-brown to blackish on the upper surface with a dark stripe down the centre of its back, and sometimes has a yellow belly. Unfortunately, the belly colour is not a reliable guide to identification as it may sometimes be creamish white, a phase characteristic of females and immature males. The gliding membrane extends from the hand to the ankle, while the tail is long and bushy, grey at the base and black at the tip, as are the hands and feet.

It is solitary or may occur in pairs. It is a tree-dweller, coming out at night to feed on nectar, sap and insects. It also licks freshly-exuded gum from Manna Gums. It is more active than the Greater Glider when in the tree and often hangs upside-down like a sloth. When volplaning it gives a whirring moan on take-off, followed by a long gurgling shriek. It may glide more than a hundred yards.

GENUS *Schoinobates* (Greater Glider)

Greater Glider *Schoinobates volans*
This medium-sized, robust glider is the largest of the gliding possums and occurs along the coastal highlands of eastern Australia from Townsville in Queensland to Melbourne in Victoria. Another subspecies, *S. minor*, occurs from Townsville to above Cooktown.

The head, body, limbs and tail are normally black, while the undersurface is white. The tail is long and bushy. The gliding membrane extends from the elbow to the ankle. This species is related to the ring-tailed possum group.

Generally a solitary animal, it may also be found in pairs, living in trees and coming out at night to feed on leaves and shoots of certain eucalypts. It has also been known to eat the leaves and blossoms off apple trees. A feature which assists in locating this animal at night are its eyes, which reflect like jewels in strong torchlight. When gliding, it can cover distances of up to forty yards.

In Victoria, birth has been reported in July and August. Although there are two teats, only one minute naked baby is born. After four months the youngster leaves the pouch and rides on the mother's back.

GENUS *Pseudocheirus* (Ring-tailed Possums)

Although a great number of species and subspecies of ring-tailed possums are listed by the authors of our mammal books, they are all very similar in form and colouration. Generally they extend from the northern part of the Northern Territory to Cape York and down the eastern coast to South Australia. A race occurs in Tasmania and another may be found in south-western Western Australia. They prefer rain forest, sclerophyll forest or woodland areas, where they shelter during the day in hollow branches or in a nest of leaves. They come out at night to feed on leaves, trees and shrubs. They are solitary animals, but are common over most of their range.

Ring-tailed Possum *Pseudocheirus peregrinus*

This is a medium-sized, stout animal with a short head, pointed muzzle and short round ears with a white patch behind. The head, limbs and body are reddish or grey while the belly is grey-white. The tail is tapered and prehensile with a naked patch on the lower surface, and the end one-third is white.

They are quarrelsome animals, and do not take well to captivity. Their staring eyes are adapted to the night so that they do not like coming out during the day. Their call is a bird-like note repeated several times. They grunt loudly when fighting. They breed once a year in the early months, with a litter of two. The young leave the pouch at the end of April.

Pseudocheirus peregrinus occurs down the east coast of Australia from north Queensland to Victoria and South Australia.

The sooty-grey or smoky-brown Tasmanian form (*convolutor*), and the Western Australian form (*occidentalis*) are probably merely variants of this species.

The following appear to be more distinct:

P. archeri occurs also near Cairns in northern Queensland. It is greenish, tinged with definite striping and glistening golden-tinted hairs on the back.

P. dahli occurs in western Arnhem Land. It is a rock-dweller which has forsaken trees for granite country. It cannot oppose the first two digits of the hand to the remaining three. It also has a very short tail, naked at the tip, and a dark dorsal stripe.

Ring-tailed Possum

GENUS *Hemibelideus*

Lemur-like Ring-tailed Possum *Hemibelideus lemuroides*
This rather agile possum, which seems to be superficially unlike any of our other possums, may be found in a small region near Cairns in dense rain-forest where it builds a nest amongst branches of high trees. The generic name means 'semi-glider', but although definite gliding membranes are missing it is known to leap from high to lower branches with its long bushy tail acting as a rudder. It feeds on buds and leaves.

This species most closely resembles the Greater Glider in form, skull shape, and dentition. The skull is shorter and broader than that of any ring-tail. Some scientists regard this species as a transition between the ring-tailed possums and the Greater Glider.

In form, it is lemur-like, with a short, blunt head and a robust build. The head and body are grizzled chocolate-brown while the belly is greyish-yellow. The long bushy tail is dark-brown with a small one-inch naked area on the underside of the tip.

These animals, because of their nocturnal and furtive habits are said to be very uncommon, but this belief may be due to the difficulty of obtaining specimens from dark dense scrubs.

GENUS *Trichosurus* (Brush-tailed Possums)

These possums are distinguished from all others by the thick brushy tail which, together with their pointed snouts and long ears, suggested the name 'Vulpine (fox-like) Opposum' to the naturalist who first described one.

Although the tail is brushy, it has a naked prehensile area under the tip, as in ring-tails. The broad sturdy skull and the smooth, mound-like cusps on the molars, also distinguish the species.

The most attractive, thick, close, woolly fur, combined with the prevalence of the genus, once led to the exploitation of these possums for the fur trade. Unlike the most valuable fur animals in other countries, the possums were not bred in captivity. They were killed in their wild state, so that no check could be made on their depletion. When removed from the protected list in South Australia between June and September 1920, over 100,000 were killed for the fur trade. They were marketed under such names as 'Opposum', 'Beaver', 'Adelaide Chinchilla', and when sheared and dyed, as 'Skunk'. In the 1931–2 season over one million skins were exported from South Australia, many of which were from animals caught by snares or killed by cyanide poison.

Brush-tailed Possum *Trichosurus vulpecula*

The various forms of this species may be found widely distributed from north Queensland through NSW and Victoria to South Australia. Others may be found in south-western Western Australia, the Kimberleys, and Arnhem Land of northern Australia, Tasmania and Kangaroo Island. It may be found in both dry sclerophyll forest and open woodland. In open plain areas and especially in the inland, it occurs in trees lining the banks of perennial rivers. It nests in the hollow branches of trees.

This animal is well known in many of the wooded outer suburbs of our towns, for it often comes down at night to feed on scraps of bread and cake left out by humans. Generally Brush-tailed Possums are solitary. They eat leaves, buds, shoots and native fruits of trees and shrubs. In NSW the female gives birth to a single young between March and September. The youngster becomes independent after about 150 days.

The other species of Brush-tailed Possum is the **Short-eared Brush-tailed Possum** *Trichosurus caninus*, which occurs from southern coastal Queensland through the coastal region of NSW into Victoria. It can be distinguished by its short rounded ears, which are as broad as they are high. The rich dense fur is only rivalled amongst marsupials by that of the Tasmanian Brush-tail.

Top: Short-eared Brush-tail Possum (p. 64). Below: Ring-tail Possum (p. 62)

Top: Female Sugar Glider and two young (p. 60). Below: Feather-tail Glider (p. 52)

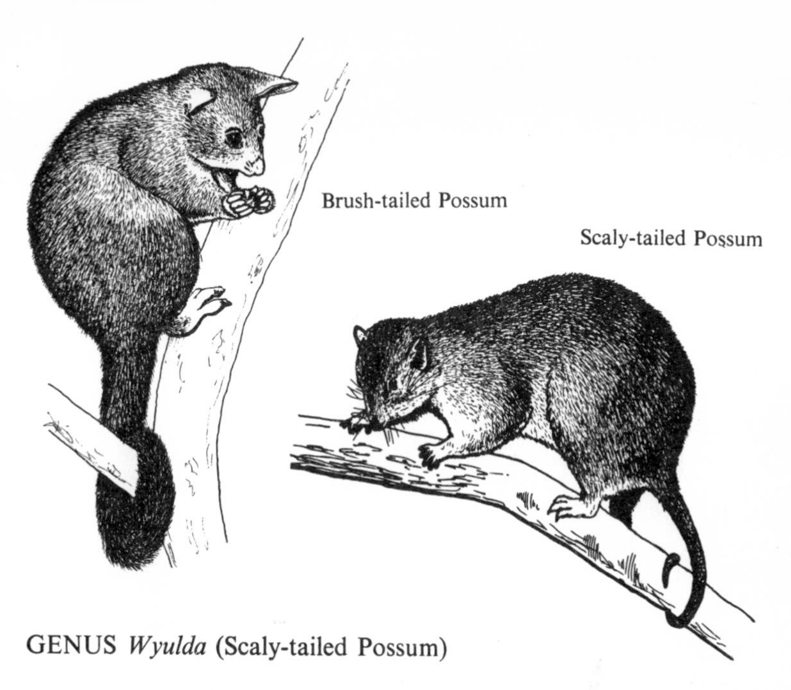

GENUS *Wyulda* (Scaly-tailed Possum)

This extremely rare species seems to provide a link between the Brush-tailed Possums and the Cuscus. The tail, completely covered by naked scales, shows, however, that this genus is separate and highly specialized.

Scaly-tailed Possum *Wyulda squamicaudata*
This species is known from only three adult specimens and one juvenile, all found in the Kimberly region of north-western Western Australia. It appears to prefer savannah woodland, where it shelters amongst rock crevices during the day. As far as is known it is solitary. It clambers amongst rocks and climbs trees, coming out at night to feed. Its habits are supposed to be very similar to that of the rock-haunting Ring-tailed Possum from northern Australia.

It is medium-sized and stockily built. The head is short while the ears are rounded. The head and the body are pale grey becoming brown on the rump, while the undersurface is yellowish. A dark stripe runs from the shoulders to the rump. The whole tail is naked, prehensile, and completely covered with oval scales which do not overlap.

GENUS *Phalanger* (Cuscuses)

In these large possums the terminal half of the prehensile tail is naked and covered with rasp-like scales. They have very small ears which barely jut above the fur. Cuscuses occur from Timor and the Celebes, through New Guinea to Cape York in Australia.

Spotted Cuscus *Phalanger maculatus*
This slow sluggish animal from the extreme tip of Cape York occurs in both open woodland and rainforest areas where it curls up asleep in thick foliage during the day. At night it becomes more active, but still moves about slowly, devouring large quantities of leaves. It is also carnivorous, eating small birds and other small mammals. This makes it more carnivorous than other Australian possums.

The female Spotted Cuscus is grey all over, with a yellowish-white belly. The male Cuscus has irregular white spots on the upper surface.

The Cuscus is strictly nocturnal and arboreal. There are four teats in the pouch, which may contain between two and four young; it is said that a female is hardly ever found without at least one youngster in the pouch.

Another closely related species is the **Grey Cuscus** *Phalanger orientalis*, which occurs in rocky scrubs near the McIlwraith Range in central Cape York, Queensland, as well as New Guinea. Both sexes are grey and unspotted, with a dark central stripe extending from between the ears to the rump.

FAMILY PHASCOLARCTIDAE (Koala)

The Koala is a highly specialized animal combining many characteristics of possums and wombats, and presenting the extreme example of adaptation to tree climbing. In this, it is similar to the tailless sloths and tailless monkeys of other countries. This adaptation has also led to a similarity of hand structure and dentition in the koala and the ring-tailed possums. The lack of a prehensile tail is hard to explain. The fact that the koala and the wombat have similar rudimentary, though muscular, tails is not by itself convincing evidence of common ancestry. The lack of a tail in the koala may indicate that the animals were once ground-dwellers.

The pouch of the koala is not similar to that of any of the possums. It opens backwards, not forwards, and contains only two teats, as does the wombat's. Possums possess four. The koala also has functional cheek pouches, used in masticating its leafy food and similar to the rudimentary cheek pouches of the wombats. The koala and the wombat may have evolved from a common ancestral ground-dwelling stock.

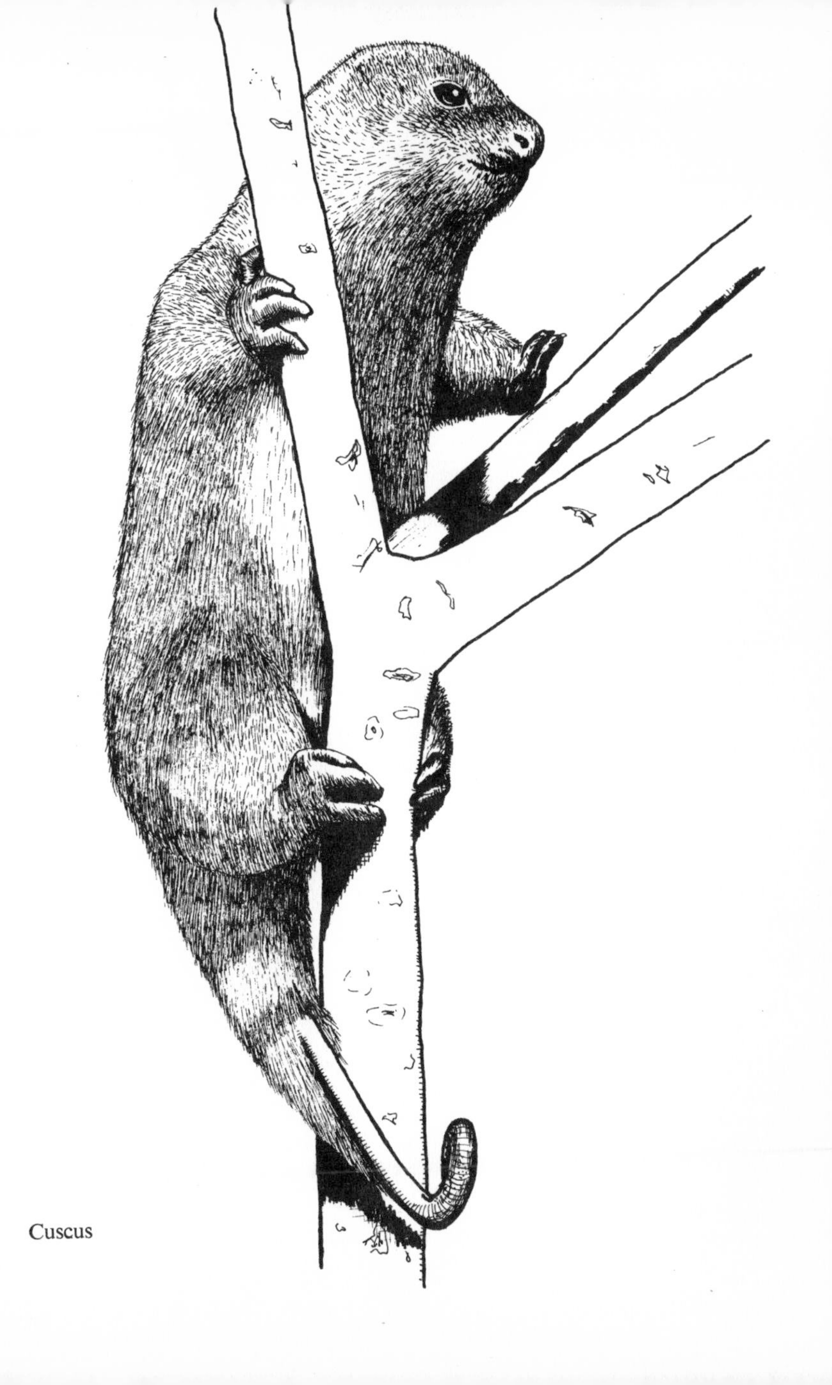

Cuscus

GENUS *Phascolarctos* (Koala)

Koala *Phascolarctos cinereus*
The koala, our most famous furred animal, may be found down the eastern coast of Australia from Townsville in Queensland, through NSW to south-western Victoria. It extends inland to the western slopes of the Great Dividing Range. Its favourite habitat is dry sclerophyll forest or woodland where it rests during the day in the fork of a tree.

The koala is a slow, solitary animal (sometimes found in small groups) that lives in trees. It feeds entirely on leaves and shoots of eucalypts from about twelve species but prefers blue and grey gums in NSW and Manna Gums in Victoria. Koalas eat about two-and-a-half pounds of foliage a day. The structure which allows the koala to consume such a bulky diet is its 'appendix' or elongated intestine which attains a length of about seven feet. Koalas seldom drink water, and the term 'koala' was borrowed from an aboriginal word which meant 'no drink'.

In form, the koala is large and bear-like, with fluffy ears and a bulbous snout. The head and body are dark grey and the rump dirty white. The undersurface of the koala is grey-white.

Koalas breed every second year. A single young is born after a gestation period of 35 days. The youngster is three-quarters of an inch long and weighs five and a half grammes at birth. It uses the mother's pouch for two or more months before climbing on to her back where it remains until a year old. The koala is full grown at four years.

Top: Tasmanian Brush-tail Possums (p. 64). Below: Common Wombat (p. 73)

FAMILY VOMBATIDAE (Wombats)

Wombats are extremely specialized animals, showing obvious traces of relationship to the arboreal possums and the koala. They are similar in both form and dentition to the Beaver from America. Their teeth are remarkably rodent-like. They have only a single pair of upper and lower incisors and all the teeth are rootless. These teeth grow continually, which stops them from being ground away by constant use.

Wombats are prodigious diggers in rough country. With their large, powerful build, shovel-like claws, and sharp incisors, they can make their way through the toughest roots and hardest soil. Wombats dig with their claws while lying on their side and throwing the dirt out with their hindfeet. Some of these burrows have measured up to a hundred feet long, but usually they are ten to fifteen feet long, with a nest lined with bark at the end.

Wombats eat grasses, bark, roots of shrubs and trees, and certain species of fungi.

GENUS *Vombatus* (Naked-nosed or Coarse-haired Wombats)

Members of this genus have coarse, harsh coats, and a naked muzzle. They also have fifteen ribs instead of thirteen as have the Hairy-nosed Wombats.

Common Wombat *Vombatus ursinus hirsutus*

The Common Wombat is a bulky, heavily-built animal with a broad blunt head, coarse grizzled brown or black fur, and powerful fore-limbs with five strong-clawed toes. It may be found along the coastal area of NSW from Grafton south to Victoria and the far south of South Australia. It prefers mountainous sclerophyll forest where it lives in burrows constructed under large rocks or trees. It is essentially a nocturnal animal, feeding on the roots and bark of certain species of trees, shrubs and grasses. In NSW the season of birth is July. The litter contains a single young.

Other closely related forms are:

Bass Strait Wombat *V. ursinus ursinus.* This wombat now only occurs on Flinders Island, but once could be found on Clarke, Cape Barren, King and Deal Islands in Bass Strait. It is the smallest wombat, growing to only two-and-a-half feet long. It is light greyish-brown.

Tasmanian Wombat *V. u. tasmaniensis.* Occurs in Tasmania and grows to about three feet in length. It may vary from dark brown in lowland areas to light greyish in mountain areas. It makes extensive burrows in sandy country and appears to be common.

GENUS *Lasiorhinus* (Hairy-nosed Wombats)

This genus contains two species, the first of which has two sub-species. The generic name, *Lasiorhinus*, refers to the hairy nose which characterises the genus. Other features are the soft and silky coat, the long, narrow ears, and the great breadth of the nasal area of the skull.

Hairy-nosed Wombat *Lasiorhinus latifrons*

This animal is similar in form to the Common Wombat except for hairy snout. It occurs across the Nullarbor Plain and near the lower Murray River in South Australia. It may be found in open plains or mallee areas, where it shelters during the day in extensive communal warrens dug beneath shelves of limestone rock.

The Hairy-nosed Wombat is a docile animal and is retreating rapidly from the extension of settlement. It feeds on roots, bark and grasses.

Queensland Hairy-nosed Wombat *L.* (*Wombatula*) *gillespiei* is a species once common in hilly areas of southern-central Queensland. This species is said to show intermediate features between *Vombatus* and *Lasiorhinus*, and is sometimes regarded as a member of a separate genus, *Wombatula*.

Other Queensland specimens have been described as a subspecies of *L. latifrons*.

▲ Brush-tailed Rock-Wallaby (p. 91)

Agile Wallaby (p. 96) ▼

▼ Female Pretty-face Wallaby (p. 96)

▲ Yellow-footed Wallabies
▼ Sandv Wallaby

Dama Wallabies (p. 98) ▼
Black-gloved Wallabies (p. 100) (Lower)

FAMILY MACROPODIDAE (Rat kangaroos, Wallabies, Kangaroos, etc.)

These animals form a division of essentially herbivorous marsupials with enlarged hindlimbs and seemingly reduced forelimbs. With the enlargement of the hindlimbs came the development of the tail which acted as a third leg or balance, or was used to slowly push the body along when the animal was grazing.

Kangaroo and wallaby teeth are adapted for grass eating. The front teeth are suited to snipping off herbage, while the broad-crowned, sharp-ridged, molars behind are for chewing. A space exists between the two types of teeth so that the tongue can freely manipulate the food in the mouth. The rat-kangaroos are not so exclusively grazers and their teeth show traces of insectivorous dentition.

The kangaroo family contains a large number of genera and species. These fall into two main divisions. The first sub-family, Potoroinae, contains the rat-kangaroos. The second sub-family, Macropodinae, contains the wallabies and kangaroos.

Red or Plains Kangaroo (p. 103)

SUB-FAMILY POTOROINAE (Rat kangaroos)

GENUS *Hypsipyrmnodon* (Musk Rat-kangaroo)

This most interesting animal was once given a sub-family of its own because it seemed to provide a link between the possums and the kangaroos. Its feet, teeth and tail closely resemble those of certain possums, but other features distinguish it as a rat-kangaroo.

Musk Rat-kangaroo *Hypsiprymnodon moschatus*
This medium-small, rat-like rat-kangaroo occurs in north-eastern Queensland along the coastal area from Mosman through Cairns to Townsville, and extending inland to the Atherton Tableland. It prefers rainforest areas where it runs rather than leaps, through dense damp brushes and scrubs. It is partly diurnal, and eats insects and vegetable matter which it scratches from litter on the forest floor. It is a hard animal to observe, but the noise that it makes while scratching for food reveals its presence.

The Musk Rat-kangaroo is grizzled rufous-brown on the head and the body, while the undersurface is greyish brown. Striking features are the five-toed hindfoot, with a movable but clawless first toe which is not completely opposable, and the hairless, scaled tail. The head and the body are ten inches long, while the tail is six-and-a-half inches long. It appears to be uncommon over most of its range.

The rest of the sub-family includes the remaining rat-kangaroos, which lack the first toe of the hind-foot. The teeth of this group are still primitive compared with the larger true kangaroos. They possess canine teeth, which are either absent or minute in the larger animals.

Rat-kangaroos tend to be difficult to classify, due to their similarity of form. The following four genera may be distinguished by this key:

(A) Have the upper and lower premolar (first cheek tooth) channelled by six or more deep grooves:
1. With a naked muzzle tip; large openings in the palate; and much inflated ear bones .... *Bettongia*
2. With a partly hairy muzzle tip; bony palate almost complete; and outer ear bones little inflated .... *Aepyprymnus*

(B) Have the upper premolar marked with less than six grooves:
1. Having the hindfoot shorter than the head and strong canine teeth .... *Potorous*
2. Having the hindfoot longer than the head and minute canines .... *Caloprymnus*

GENUS *Bettongia* (Short-nosed Rat-kangaroos)

Four species are included in this genus. They all have a naked, flesh-coloured, muzzle tip; short rounded ears; large nails on the hands; hindfeet longer than the head. The tail generally is crested, while the stout skull has large openings in the palate. The first cheek tooth is grooved, with from six to about twelve channels.

Brush-tailed Rat-kangaroo *Bettongia penicillata*
A medium-sized, slender-built rat-kangaroo which was once widely spread over southern Australia from north-eastern New South Wales to the western Australian coast. It survives in the south-west corner of Western Australia.

Its colour is grey-brown on the head and body, while the under-surface is white. The prehensile tail is crested with black hairs. The forefeet have five toes, each with a claw, while the long hindfeet have only four toes, with the second and third toes fused.

The Brush-tailed Rat-kangaroo is a solitary nocturnal animal with a bounding run. Its diet includes some ground insects. The animals are also excellent scavengers. They build their nests under vegetation, pulling grass or leaves over the entrance. They have a most unusual habit of carrying nesting material coiled up in their tails. The litter is a single young, but breeding may take place at any time of the year.

Related species are:

Rufous Rat-kangaroo

Lesueur's Rat-kangaroo *Bettongia lesueur*
Once distributed across dry parts of temperate Australia, this species has now gone from eastern regions. It has soft fur and the tail is not crested. Families live in larger burrows.

The third species is **Gaimard's Rat-kangaroo** *Bettongia gaimardi* which occurs widely in Tasmania where it favours grassy plains and stony ridges on the outskirts of forests. It is larger and more grizzled-grey coloured, with the tail tipped white. Its grassy nests are built in a depression sheltered by a bush or large tufts of grass. Originally it occurred too in south-eastern Australia.

The fourth species, *Bettongia tropica*, is confined to north-eastern Queensland. It resembles *B. penicillata* but has skull and teeth differences.

GENUS *Aepyprymnus*

Rufous Rat-kangaroo *Aepyprymnus rufescens*
The Rufous Rat-kangaroo is a medium-large, robust, attractive species found along the coastal regions of eastern Australia from Cairns to Newcastle in NSW. It is found mainly in open woodland, where it nests during the day under grass tussocks or at the base of bushes. If disturbed in the open it will make for a hollow log. It is rare in NSW but common in Queensland, and originally it extended south into Victoria.

It is readily distinguished by its brightly grizzled-brown colour; harsher hair mingled with silver-white hairs; whitish hip stripe; black-backed ears; hairy muzzle tip; complete bony palate, and an uncrested, tapering tail which is not prehensile.

Potoroo

The Rufous Rat-kangaroo is a solitary animal, or occurs in small groups. It comes out to feed during the night. It digs for food with its long foreclaws which are well adapted for scratching. The head and body grow to twenty-one inches long while the tail is fifteen inches long.

GENUS *Potorous* (Long-nosed, or Broad-faced Rat-kangaroos)

There are three species in this genus, all of which are smaller and more rat-like than other genera of the sub-family Potoroinae. They are distinguished by having hindfeet which are shorter than the head, which makes them look a little un-kangaroo-like, and also results in a run similar to a gallop, instead of a hopping movement.

Potoroo *Potorous tridactylus*
This medium-sized, stoutly-built animal occurs from south-eastern Queensland to eastern Victoria. A Western Australian race (*gilberti*) is now extinct.

Potoroos prefer rainforest or wet sclerophyll forest areas, where they nest beneath debris on the forest floor. They are quick furtive animals, leaping away with a rapid hopping-gallop with the body held horizontally, at the slightest disturbance. If hard pressed they will shelter under a tree or amongst stones. They feed at night on insects and possibly roots which they dig up with their foreclaws and snout in a pig-like way.

The head and the body are dark grey-brown, while the belly is greyish white. The tail is short and tapered. The ears are round and short. The snout has a naked area of skin which extends back on the dorsal surface. Other species are:

Broad-faced Rat-kangaroo *Potorous platyops* occurs in the southern corner of Western Australia. This species has a remarkably broad and short face, which gives it a bluff appearance, and no naked skin area on top of the muzzle. This primitive member of the kangaroo family is now presumably extinct.

The third species, *Potorous apicalis*, occurs in southern Victoria, on Bass Strait islands and in Tasmania. It resembles *P. tridactylus* but the head is longer and narrower.

GENUS *Caloprymnus* (Desert or Bluff-nosed Rat-kangaroo)

The single species is distinguished by an unusual broadening between the eyes; spread upper lips; and a short, naked, conical snout. The ears are also longer and narrower, and the tail longer, than in other rat-kangaroo. The colouring is also distinctive. The strikingly grizzled fur has five distinct colour bands, including ivory yellow, cinnamon and blackish-brown. The sides are buff-yellow, while the undersurface is sandy-white. The excellent colouration forms an effective camouflage in the sandridge flats and stony areas in which it lives.

Desert Rat-kangaroo *Caloprymnus campestris*
This medium-sized, robustly built, animal occurs in an area where the Northern Territory, Queensland, and South Australian borders meet, in and near the parallel sand-ridged desert on sand and stony flats. Skeletal remains have also been recorded at Eucla on the WA–SA border.

The Desert Rat-Kangaroo has had a remarkable history of being 'lost' and 'found'. This may be due to its restricted range and to inefficient collecting methods. Normally it is scarce over most of its range but populations fluctuate greatly with favourable conditions.

Unlike many other desert-dwelling mammals, this animal does not dig burrows, but chooses to build a nest in a shallow depression under saltbush. The nest is lined with leaves and grasses and is crudely thatched over with twigs and grass stems. Although it does not construct a burrow, it is still nocturnal, coming out to feed on roots of plants and leaves growing on desert flats. It is strange that this animal has not taken to the sand-ridges where more succulent vegetation grows.

If disturbed, it will run with a very swift bounding gait, and has great staying power.

The breeding season is irregular, being totally dependent upon favourable weather conditions. The litter comprises a single young.

SUB-FAMILY MACROPODINAE
(Wallabies, Wallaroos, Kangaroos)

This group contains the herbivorous wallabies and kangaroos, which range in size from the small hare-wallabies to the very large Grey or Red Plains Kangaroos. There are three main divisions:

The first contains all the small wallabies, in which the length of the hindfoot except in the largest rock-wallabies, never exceeds six inches.

The second contains all the intermediate-sized wallabies or small kangaroos, in which the length of the hindfoot ranges from six-and-a-half-inches to ten inches.

The third group contains the true kangaroos, in which the length of the hindfoot exceeds ten inches. It includes the Wallaroos.

Features which distinguish all members of the sub-family Macropodinae from the rat-kangaroos Potoroinae are:

1. Ears elongated and oval.
2. Foreclaws not greatly elongated, or of greatly varying lengths.
3. Canine teeth rudimentary or absent—central incisors not longer than other incisors.
4. Molars, ridged transversely, grow larger toward the back of the mouth—premolar in same line as tooth row.

GENERA *Lagostrophus* and *Lagorchestes* (Hare-wallabies)

These attractive animals were named hare-wallabies by Gould because of their hare-like speed, jumping ability, and solitary habits. These solitary habits, however, are now leading to their extinction through settlement. The single species of the genus *Lagostrophus* may be distinguished from .species of the genus *Lagorchestes* by its banded colouration and naked muzzle-tip. All species of the latter genus have hairy muzzle-tips and more or less uniform colouration.

Banded Hare-wallaby *Lagostrophus fasciatus*
This medium-sized, slender-built hare-wallaby occurs on a number of islands in Shark Bay, WA. Other populations once occurred in South Australia and the south-west of Western Australia. They may be found amongst low scrub vegetation, or hidden in thickets of spiky *Mimosa* tunnelled with runs and paths in which they hide at the slightest disturbance. They run with a swift bounding gait. This beautiful wallaby was first recorded by William Dampier in 1699.

The thickly-furred head and body are grizzled-grey, with the rump banded black and white, while the belly is greyish-white. The tail is grey, thinly haired and tapering. The forefeet have five toes, the hindfeet have four. The head and body are 18 inches long, and the tail 13 inches.

Brown Hare-wallaby *Lagorchestes leporides*
This slender-built, medium-sized, hare-wallaby once occurred widely over the interior of NSW, Victoria and South Australia. They are now very rare or perhaps extinct. They preferred open grassland or saltbush plains. If disturbed, they ran with a rapid bounding gait.

Brown Hare-wallabies have a hairy snout and a rufous patch around the eye. They are pale brown on the head and body while the belly is yellow-grey. A black patch occurs on the elbow. The tapered tail is sparsely haired. The head and body are 20 inches long and the tail 13 inches.

Another closely related species is the Western Hare-Wallaby *Lagorchestes hirsutus* which originally occurred in the interior of south-western WA. It lacks the black elbow patch. This is a shaggy species with long reddish hairs thickly intermingled over the lower back area near the tail.

Populations of the species are found on Bernier and Dorre Islands outside Shark Bay.

Another more common species is the Spectacled Hare-Wallaby *Lagorchestes conspicillatus*, which occurs on Barrow Island off the WA coast between Onslow and Roebourne, and across tropical Australia to eastern Queensland. It has more conspicuous reddish spectacles.

Wallaroo or Euro (p. 102)

▲ Red-necked Pademelon (p. 94)
▼ Head of male Grey Kangaroo

Red Kangaroo (p. 103) ▲
Red Kangaroo relaxing ▼

▲ Head of male Red Kangaroo (p. 103)
▼ Head of female Red Kangaroo (p. 103)

GENUS *Dendrolagus* (Tree Kangaroos)

Tree-kangaroos have undergone a reversal of evolution by re-ascending trees to live as their ancestors did before they took to the ground and developed a kangaroo-like form.

Features which distinguish these quaint animals are the limbs, which are more equal in length; cushion-like rough-skinned soles; strong sharp claws on both the fore- and hind-feet for grasping branches, and a long, slender, non-prehensile tail used as a balance and prop while climbing.

Tree-kangaroos are typical of the mammal fauna of New Guinea, and the two species found in Australia entered from New Guinea via Cape York. They occur in the mountainous and tableland region of north-eastern Queensland near Cairns. They are forest-loving creatures, living for most of the time in trees which they climb with amazing agility. They are also known to make fantastic leaps of thirty feet with great sureness. The males of both species tend to be very pugnacious.

Lumholtz's Tree-kangaroo *Dendrolagus lumholtzi*

This large, stockily built, tree-kangaroo lives in the Cairns (Qld) district in mountainous rain-forest country where it shelters in the thick forest roof.

It is grey-fawn on the back, while the face is dark with a pale band across the forehead. The undersurface is pale white with the fore- and hindfeet black. The tail is long, slender and not prehensile. The forefeet have five toes, each with a sharp claw; the short hind-feet have four toes.

Lumholtz's Tree-kangaroo lives in small groups in the forest canopy and seems to prefer a single species of tall, slender, tree which is plentiful at the crest of the range. The group consists of a male and

◀ Female Grey Kangaroo (p. 104)

a number of attendant females. During the day they curl up in the crowns of the trees and at night feed on leaves, ferns, creepers and wild fruits.

A closely related species is **Bennett's Tree-kangaroo** *Dendrolagus bennettianus*, which occurs in rain forest of the mountainous coastal area near Daintree and Cooktown in northern Queensland. It is duller in colour, with a rufous patch at the base of the tail.

Lumholtz's Tree Kangaroo (p. 89)

Brush-tailed Rock-wallaby

GENERA *Petrogale* and *Peradorcas* (Rock-Wallabies)

These small wallabies occur in rocky range and outcrop country throughout Australia. Their habitat has modified their hindfeet and tails to suit the environment. The tail is long and more-or-less long-haired and it acts as a balancer, while the hindfeet have become padded and granulated to prevent wear and slippage.

These Rock-wallabies are prodigous leapers and exceptionally sure-footed in rocky and precipitous areas. During the hottest part of the day they rest in cool haunts amongst ledges and under overhangs of rock. Their excellent camouflage makes them difficult to detect while sitting in front of a rock face. If disturbed, they can leap away in a flash. When sheltering in a retreat they rely heavily on their camouflage, and thus become easy prey to wild dogs and large pythons.

Rock-wallabies eat grass and the leaves of shrubs, and can live without free water for considerable periods.

Brush-tailed Rock-wallaby *Petrogale penicillata*
This large, stockily-built, dark-coloured wallaby is found in rocky areas of most regions of Australia as well as on off-shore islands. It is found mainly in mountainous dry sclerophyll forest country resting in caves and rocky crevices during the heat of the day. It feeds on vegetation during the cool of the evening and at night.

It is typically dark grey-brown on the head and body, while the belly is yellowish-brown. A white cheek stripe runs along the face and a black mark occurs near the armpit. The black tail is strongly brushed for its full length; it is not tapered and has a rufous base.

These animals are a popular tourist attraction at the Jenolan Caves (Vic.), where they may be found leaping amongst rocks near the Grand Arch.

Other closely related species are:

Ring-tailed Rock-wallaby *Petrogale xanthopus*

It occurs in the Gawler and Flinders Ranges in South Australia. It is the largest and most striking of the genus, distinguished by ring markings on the tail. Is also called the Yellow-footed Rock-wallaby. Other populations occur as far north as the Bulloo River district in south-western Queensland near Avadale, where their colour is browner and the tail only faintly ringed.

Rothschild's Rock-wallaby *Petrogale rothschildi*

This wallaby occurs on a small isolated area near Roebourne on coastal Western Australia. Has a dark head and ears; a white patch behind the shoulder; no dark neck stripe.

Little Rock-wallaby *Peradorcas concinna*

This medium-sized, slender-built animal may be found in northern Australia in the Kimberly Region and Arnhem Land. This is the smallest Rock-wallaby and is distinguished by its slight build, bright orange-rufous colouration and distinctive molar teeth which slide towards the front of the mouth in the jaw socket to replace teeth which have fallen out in front.

The Little Rock-wallaby is orange-rufous on the head and body, while the belly is greyish-white. The thickly-haired tail is reddish-grey at the base, but dark-tipped. The snout is naked, and the ear quite short.

The animals occur singly or in small groups amongst scrub vegetation in rocky range country. They are agile rock climbers, feeding at dusk or during the night on vegetation.

GENUS *Onychogalea* (Nail-tail Wallabies)

The three silky-haired wallabies of this group possess a minute nail at the tip of their tails. There seems to be no explanation for the function of this nail and unfortunately the two southern species are becoming extinct, thus denying scientists the opportunity to observe the use of this appendage.

These little animals are residents of tussocky plains or rock-strewn scrub in during the cool of the evening or early night. The long, sharp, central hand-nails are very similar to those of rat-kangaroos, which suggests they may have a similar diet.

The imported fox and the rabbit are the most serious threat to the survival of these species in the south and east of Australia. They are now on the verge of extinction.

Bridled Nail-tail Wallaby *Onychogalea fraenata*
The popular name for this species comes from the marking on its head and shoulders which suggests a bridle. The wallaby grew to about the size of a large hare, and occurred in inland areas of eastern Australia from lower South Australia to about Rockhampton in Queensland. Its favourite habitat was hot, dry, pebble-strewn, shrub-covered low inland hill country and it was partially independent of water. It was herbivorous and partly diurnal. The females usually gave birth to a single young about May. It is evidently extinct now.

The Bridled Nail-tail Wallaby is grey, with a greyish-white belly. A white stripe edged with black runs from the armpits up over the back of the neck to the ears. This is the bridle marking. The tail is grey and tapering, with a black tip and a nail-like point. The forelimbs, which are held at an awkward angle to the body, are grey with black toes, while the hindlimbs are grey with white feet.

Another closely related species is the **Northern** or **Sandy Nail-tail Wallaby** *Onychogalea unguifer*

O. unguifer occurs in northern Australia from the Kimberly region across to Arnhem Land and the Gulf Country of Queensland. This animal is the largest of the three species. It is the least conspicuously marked, but is more brightly coloured. It is found in sandy or limestone country.

A second closely-related species is the **Crescent Nail-tail Wallaby** *Onychogalea lunata*. This species used to occur from south-western Australia across central Australia to the lower Darling region of New South Wales. It was smaller, more delicate, and had only a crescent marking near the shoulder instead of the bridle marking. This species may now be extinct.

GENERA *Setonix* and *Thylogale* (Scrub or Pademelon Wallabies)

Pademelons form one of the three major groups of kangaroos. The term pademelon is mainly associated with the earliest discovered scrub wallaby, *Thylogale thetis*, from eastern Australia, where these small wallabies have their richest variety and numbers. Pademelons have a hindfoot which does not exceed six inches; the basal length of the skull does not exceed four-and-a-half inches.

Pademelons live amongst thick scrub, dense forest undergrowth or thick vegetation in swampy areas. They graze at dusk and early mornings on green grass growing on slopes and flats near thickets. They also take leaves and shoots.

As with other kangaroos, they breed slowly and have only a single young in a year. Pademelons have been trapped and hunted wantonly because their soft fur makes good rugs and trimmings.

Red-legged Pademelon *Thylogale stigmatica*
This species may be found along the coastal strip of eastern Australia from Cape York to Newcastle NSW.

It may be found in rainforest areas or wet sclerophyll forest regions, where it shelters in thicket runways. They are solitary animals or occur in small groups feeding at night on vegetation.

Typically, *T. stigmatica* has short, brilliantly-coloured fur, with rust-coloured legs. The nape is greyish. Has an indistinct dark neck stripe and a yellowish-white hip-stripe.

Other closely related species are:
Red-necked Pademelon *Thylogale thetis*

Occurs commonly from Bundaberg Qld south along the coastal region to Moruya NSW. This is the common pademelon of the early colonists. Has a rufous neck and grey-brown heels.

Tasmanian or **Red-bellied Pademelon** *Thylogale billardieri*

Occurs abundantly in Tasmania and some islands in Bass Strait, but its mainland populations (Victoria and South Australia) are now extinct. Has a dusky greyish-brown back and a yellowish undersurface; a long soft, shaggy coat; no face marks; short ears and short tail. It is gregarious.

Quokka

Quokka or **Short-tailed Pademelon** *Setonix brachyurus*
This medium sized, stockily-built, kangaroo-like animal was once found widely in coastal areas of south-western Western Australia. Now it may only be found in small isolated mainland areas and in large numbers only on Rottnest and Bald Islands off the Western Australian coast. It prefers coastal thickets and swamp areas in thick tea-tree scrub and tussock grass.

The Quokka may be distinguished by its size (smaller than a hare); short tapering tail; short foot; short, rounded ears hardly projecting above the fur, and a shaggy sombre coat. The permanent premolar, with a well marked inner edge and three or four vertical outer grooves, is double the length of the upper incisor and is as wide at the front as the back. The dentition is similar to that of the Tree-kangaroos and some wallabies of New Guinea.

The Quokka has a grey-brown head and body, while the belly is grey. They are solitary animals or occur in small groups running through mazes in coarse grass or dense undergrowth. Because their ears and hindlegs are so short, they are often mistaken for large rats. They breed between February and July, and have one young to a litter.

GENUS *Wallabia* (Brush Wallabies)

Wallabies are the medium-sized animals of the kangaroo group. The length of their feet is between 6½ and 10 inches, and the length of the base of the skull is between 4¼ and 5¼ inches. Generally they are graceful, beautiful, long-tailed animals; often richly coloured and distinctly marked. Wallabies can also be distinguished by having a well marked notch placed centrally in the third upper incisor. Wallabies spend much time grazing in tall, sparse, brushwood on high ridges.

Swamp Wallaby *Wallabia bicolor*

This large, shaggy-coated, stockily-built animal occurs commonly from Cape York down the east coast of Australia to south-western Victoria. They range on to the higher western slopes of the Great Dividing Range. Although often found in damp places, such as near Mangrove swamps, they usually haunt hillsides and moist mountain tops in country ranging from rainforest to dry sclerophyll forest.

The head and body are dark rufous-grey, while the belly is rusty yellow. The tail is black, with a dark grey base. The fore- and hind-feet are dark brown.

Sandy or **Agile Wallaby** *Wallabia agilis*

This brightly coloured, large, robust wallaby occurs across northern Australia from Broome in Western Australia to coastal east Queensland. It is to be found mainly in open woodland areas and is common over most of its range. During the morning and the evenings near the coast this wallaby grazes in the long grass of the meandering creek flats, dashing to dense tropical cover if disturbed.

The snout of the Sandy or Agile Wallaby is partly hairy between the nostrils, while the coat is rather short and coarse, almost lacking in underfur.

Whiptail or **Pretty-face Wallaby** *Wallabia parryi*

This large, slender wallaby occurs along the eastern coast of Australia from Cooktown south to Stroud in NSW. It occurs in richly grassed woodland or sclerophyll forest in open upland country. It may be distinguished by its long, slender tail, naked snout, and distinct white face stripe.

Pretty-face Wallaby

Swamp Wallaby

Agile Wallaby

Pretty-face Wallabies are regarded as being faster, more gregarious, and more diurnal than any other brush-wallaby. They can be easily approached and are loath to run from danger while grazing. Their large camps may be easily approached when they are resting during the heat of the day.

The Pretty-face Wallaby has a greyish head and body and a greyish-white belly. The ear base is brown, and a white stripe runs along the side of the face. The tail is grey, except for a small black tip. These wallabies tend to be more common in Queensland than in NSW.

Dama Wallaby or **Tammar** *Wallabia eugenii*
This medium-large, slender-built wallaby with a naked snout may be found on a number of islands and mainland areas of southern Australia. It is extinct on the South Australian mainland but still plentiful on Kangaroo Island.

The Dama Wallaby is grizzled-grey on the head and body, while the belly is grey-white. A faint dark stripe runs down the centre of the back, and the shoulders are reddish. The tail is grey, but tipped black.

The habits of the Dama Wallaby are characteristic of pademelon wallabies throughout coastal and insular Australia. It is well-known that they use distinct paths through thick scrub leading to open grassy grazing areas. They rest in a hunchback fashion with their tails jutting forward between their legs.

Black-striped Wallaby *Wallabia dorsalis*
This large, slender animal with a dark dorsal stripe, white hip-stripe and naked snout, occurs from Rockhampton in southern Queensland, due south to Tamworth in inland NSW. It may be found in both dry sclerophyll forest and woodland and is abundant in brigalow scrub and lantana patches. In southern Queensland it is considered to be the most numerous and gregarious member of the kangaroo family, in spite of the great numbers killed by shooters. Here it prefers dense scrubs and jungle areas, living in a similar fashion to pademelons or small scrub wallabies. In the brushes and scrubs, it is a shy and secretive nocturnal animal which never comes out into the open.

Red-necked Wallaby

Red-necked Wallaby *Wallabia rufogrisea*

This large, slender-built wallaby was originally described from King Island in Bass Strait. Other populations occur in Tasmania and Flinders Island, while on the mainland it ranges from Bundaberg in southern Queensland down the east coastal area to Mt. Gambier in South Australia. It is common over most of its range and may be found in dry sclerophyll forest and brush or heath country of low coastal tablelands.

The head and body are blue-grey with the nape and shoulders tinged reddish, while the belly is pale grey. There is an indistinct pale white hip stripe but no dorsal stripe. The tail is grey with a black tip.

This browsing wallaby has large, powerful incisor teeth, with an unusually wide third incisor which has a notch in the centre of the outer surface. The head and body grow to 42 inches, while the tail is 30 inches.

Black-gloved Wallaby *Wallabia irma*
This large, slender, beautiful wallaby occurs in south-western Western Australia from Esperence north to Geraldton. It prefers dry sclerophyll forest areas throughout its range, where it tends to be common. It may be distinguished by its dark-tipped ears, black crested tail, black hands and feet, and yellow cheek-stripe. The head and body are blue-grey, while the belly is pale grey. On the side of the body a pale hip-stripe occurs, and there is a suggestion of light and dark grey banding on the lower back.

Black-gloved Wallaby

The Black-gloved Wallaby resembles kangaroos, rather than the small wallabies, in its habits. It favours open forest areas covered with low scrub, and takes refuge if disturbed while feeding in nearby open grassy patches. It is a speedy, active and agile wallaby, and has earned the doubtful compliment of the 'best sporting animal' in Western Australia.

Parma Wallaby *Wallabia parma*

This large, slender animal with a naked snout once occurred in two areas of NSW; one near Wollongong, the other at Dorrigo near Coff's Harbour. It occurred in both rainforest and wet sclerophyll forest, but is extremely rare, if not extinct, over most of its range. It is a southern relative of the Black-striped Wallaby, *Wallabia dorsalis.*

The Parma Wallaby is similar to the Black-striped Wallaby but lacks a white hip stripe, or such a dark dorsal stripe. It is more rufous about the shoulders and back and has a white cheek stripe. The head and body are twenty-six inches long; the tail is seventeen inches.

Toolache Wallaby *Wallabia greyii*

This large, slender wallaby had a very restricted range in South Australia and is now extinct. It was an eastern relative of the Black-gloved Wallaby, *W. irma.* It occurred on the tip of Eyre Peninsula and the extreme south-east corner of South Australia. It was found in open woodland, till human occupation dispersed large colonies.

This wallaby was probably the most elegant of the kangaroo family. It had a fawn-grey head and body and a grey-white belly. A white stripe could be found on both the cheek and the hip. The rump was distinctly banded with between ten and twelve faint grey bars. The grey tail was tipped whitish. The head and body grew to 32 inches; the tail was 29 inches.

The Toolache Wallaby preferred well grassed open country for both feeding and resting areas. It was the fleetest of all the wallabies, and like the Black-gloved Wallaby of Western Australia was considered excellent sport.

GENUS *Macropus* (Large Kangaroos)

In Kangaroos the hindfoot, without the nail, measures more than ten inches long.

Kangaroos can be divided into three main divisions determined by their habitat. These are (a) the powerful, rugged, wallaroos of the mountain ranges, both coastal and inland; (b) the swift, long-limbed Red Plains Kangaroo of the vast inland plains and (c) the great Grey Kangaroo group of the open forest regions of eastern and southern Australia.

By examining the muzzle of a kangaroo-sized marsupial its correct grouping can be determined. The Grey Kangaroo has a completely haired muzzle, while the Red Plains Kangaroo has a small naked area between the nostrils. The Wallaroo has a naked and scaly muzzle, similar to that of a dog.

The hind-quarter area of kangaroos incorporates powerful hindlimbs to propel the bulky body. The tail is also very strong. It is able to support the whole weight of the animal if it is cornered, allowing it to use both hindlimbs in a fight. The tail also acts as a balance when the kangaroo is in full flight, or can be used to push the body along slowly while the animal is grazing. Kangaroos, unlike humans, continue to grow in size with age. Some old males may grow to above seven feet in height. These males can be rough and savage and should not be cornered.

In many parts of Australia, kangaroos are being hunted for their skins and meat. In certain parts of Western Australia hundreds are shot in a night, yet only the better portions of the carcase are taken while the rest is left to rot. Kangaroos cannot stand this constant slaughter, for they only breed once a year and at the present rate of destruction must certainly be driven to extinction.

Wallaroo or **Euro** or **Hill Kangaroo** *Macropus robustus*

The Wallaroo is a very large, stocky, powerfully-built rock-kangaroo, distributed widely over Australia in mountainous and hill country.

Wallaroos are agile rock-kangaroos which may be found in small groups lying high in rock outcrops during the day. At night they descend to the flats to feed on the grasses.

The typical Wallaroo belongs to eastern Australia, ranging from about the Victorian border northward well into Queensland. Males are sombre brownish-black and females more bluish. Old animals tend towards yellowish tones. The coat is shaggy, and animals have a habitual "stoop".

The populations of Central and South Australia are more reddish in colour, and the name Euro is usually applied to them.

Western Australian populations, also known as Euros, are dark grey or reddish brown.

There are two related species:

M. bernardus occurs in rough hill country and ranges about the headwaters of the South Alligator River NT. It is a small, sooty

Wallaroo

blackish-brown wallaby, perfectly suited to the rough rocky environment.

M. antilopinus occurs in rocky ranges of northern Australia, from northern WA to Cape York Peninsula. It has a richly-coloured short-haired coat similar to that of the Red Kangaroo. Distinguished by lack of white face marks, the shorter, stouter limbs and tail.

Red or **Plains Kangaroo** *Macropus rufus*
This very large, but slender-built kangaroo may be found widely over much of the plains area of Australia inside the Great Dividing Range. It is not found in coastal regions where the rainfall exceeds about 25 inches per annum, nor does it extend to Tasmania. The Red Kangaroo is the most striking and best known of the kangaroo family. Generally males are a bright wine-red in colour; the female is smoky-blue and has earned the name 'blue-flier'. There may be a grading of colouration of both sexes according to location and season.

Red Kangaroos may be distinguished by having a partly-haired snout and conspicuous white marks on the muzzle. The fur on the body is short and woolly.

The Red Kangaroo is highly gregarious, occurring in groups of from two to over one hundred animals. Unfortunately these animals are being hunted in many States, and if this hunting continues it may prove disastrous to our most famous marsupial. These kangaroos feed mainly at dusk on hardier grasses and herbs. Research has found that the Red Kangaroo may be able to exist without free water by extracting moisture from the grasses it eats.

If cornered, old male Red Kangaroos can prove quite dangerous; they are able to rip and claw with both of their hindfeet while balanced on their tails.

Grey Kangaroo *Macropus giganteus*

This very large, slender, greyish kangaroo with no face marks, may be found widely over the eastern part of Australia, east of a line from about Cooktown in north-eastern Queensland to Mount Gambier in South Australia. It is also in north-eastern Tasmania. The Grey Kangaroos prefer dry sclerophyll forest or open woodland areas where it shelters during the heat of the day under the shade of trees or large rocks. It seems to be quite common over most of its range.

It is soft grey on the head and body, and the belly is whitish. The tail is the same colour as the body at the base but becomes black towards the tip. The short fur is woolly in texture.

Grey Kangaroos are well known in eastern Australia and there are not many people who have not seen one. They are gregarious and are found in groups of up to twenty animals. They feed during the twilight hours and at night on herbs and grasses.

A closely related species is *Macropus fuliginosus*, the **Sooty** or **Black-faced Kangaroo.** It is brown in general colour, with black face and feet. It ranges through the drier parts of southern Australia, from central New South Wales and western Victoria to the far south-west of Western Australia. The darkest form occurs on Kangaroo Island.

Top: Male Grey Kangaroo. Below: Female with young in pouch

FURTHER READING

Australian Academy of Science, *Biological Science: the web of life*, 1967.
Australian Encyclopaedia, The.
Brazenor, C. W., *The Mammals of Victoria*, 1950.
Davey, K., *Australian Desert Life*, Periwinkle Books, 1969.
Gould, J., *Mammals of Australia*, Vols. I & II, 1845–63.
Frith, H. J., and Calaby, J. H., *Kangaroos*, 1969.
Iredale, T., and Troughton, E., *A Check-list of Mammals Recorded from Australia*, Memoir VI, Australian Museum, 1934.
Lucas, A. H. S., and Le Souef, W. H. D., *The Animals of Australia*, 1909.
Le Souef, A. S., Burrell, H., and Troughton, E., *The Wild Animals of Australia*, 1926.
Marlow, B. J., *Marsupials of Australia*, 1965.
Marlow, B. J., 'A Survey of the Marsupials of NSW', CSIRO *Wildlife Research* 3, 1958.
Troughton, E., *Furred Animals of Australia*, 1957.
Wood-Jones, F., *The Mammals of South Australia*, 1923–4.
Victorian Naturalist, The, periodical.
Wildlife in Australia, periodical.

GLOSSARY

arboreal	living mainly in trees.
canine	relating to a dog.
carnivorous	feeding on flesh.
cusp	projection on the biting surface of a mammal's tooth.
degenerate	having reverted to lower type.
diurnal	active during daylight.
dorsal	of, on or near the back.
granular	covered with grain-like bumps.
gregarious	living in groups.
grizzled	grey-haired.
herbivorous	feeding on plants.
incisor	front tooth used for biting.
insectivorous	feeding on insects, etc.
membrane	pliable sheet-like connecting tissue.
molar	back tooth, used for grinding up food.
muzzle	portion of the head in front of the eyes.
nocturnal	active mainly at night.
palate	roof of the mouth.
prehensile	capable of grasping.
rudimentary	imperfectly developed or having no function.
rufous	reddish.
sclerophyll	plant with hard leaves.
snout	the top of the muzzle.
solitary	living alone.
steppe	plain without forest.
terminal	at the end.
terrestrial	living mainly on the ground.
torpid	dormant, sluggish.
transverse	arranged in a crosswise direction.
ventral	opposite to dorsal.
volplane	descend by gliding.

Index

SCIENTIFIC NAMES

Index

COMMON NAMES